AMAZING BABIES®

AMAZING BABIES®

Essential Movement for
Your Baby in the First Year

Beverly Stokes

Foreword by Thomas R. Verny, M.D.

MOVE
Alive MEDIA

Toronto, ON   Allenwood, NJ

Video, photograph, and illustration credits:
Video sequences from *Amazing Babies®: Moving in the First Year* by Beverly Stokes.
Illustrations by Karen Martin.
Adult movement photographs by Melanie Scott.
Cover photographs by Anne Jane Grieve.
Video sequences pages 100, 105, 110. With permission: The Discovery Channel, Canada.

National Library of Canada Cataloguing in Publication Data

Stokes, Beverly
Amazing Babies: Essential Movement for Your Baby in the First Year

Includes bibliographical references and index.
ISBN 0-9687900-0-3

1. Motor ability in infants. 2. Motor learning. 3. Movement education.
4. Parenting. 5. Early childhood education. I. Title.

RJ133.S76 2001   612.7'6'0832   C2001-900174-6

Cautionary note: although many people of all ages have greatly benefited from this developmental movement approach to learn more efficient, comfortable, and healthy ways of moving, we cannot anticipate the responses of every individual. Any participant who has a physical condition that might be affected by movement explorations should consult a health care professional before doing any of these exercises.

Book design: Pronk&Associates

Publishing consultant: Malcolm Lester & Associates

Move Alive Media Inc.
418 St. Clair Avenue E., Toronto, ON M4T 1P5
http://www.amazingbabies.com

Published simultaneously in the United States and Canada. Printed in Canada.

01 02 03   54321

To the babies of the world—our amazing mentors
who explore, communicate, and learn through body movement

What an amazing adventure it has been writing and creating this book! Based on the many years I have dedicated to the study of the movement development of babies, children, and adults, I can now share with you the dynamic developmental stories—illustrated in video vignettes—that reveal the baby's unfolding abilities in action, communication, and learning.

Foremost, thank you to the babies, parents, and grandparents whose whole-hearted commitment and joyful participation in my parent-baby groups have formed the foundation of my longitudinal infant video studies since 1985, when I founded the Center for Experiential Learning. A noteworthy thank you to the new group of babies and parents who appear on the cover of this book, and to Anne Rawson, Director of the Fairlawn Neighborhood Center, for her continuing support.

I extend my sincere appreciation to the following colleagues and associates who have had a significant influence on my work: Bonnie Bainbridge Cohen, founder of the School for Body-Mind Centering®, whose experiential work in the area of developmental movement and the body systems inspired many concepts that elucidate my work with babies, children, and adults; Marion Woodman, Jungian analyst and noted author, for the in-depth adult workshops, focusing on the foundation of the origins of human movement and the interplay between perception, consciousness, and movement, that we led together over a period of twelve years; Carl Stough, founder of the Institute of Breathing Coordination, who enriched my understanding of each person's unique breathing coordination; Ruth Bernard, founder of the Center of Movement, where my *Joy of Parenting* and *Moms and Tots* programs originated and the journey began; and Frau Til Thiele, whose kinesthetic wisdom has permeated my work from its early roots.

During the writing of the manuscript, it has been a great pleasure to have participated in the many constructive discussions of my ideas with knowledgeable movement colleagues: Vera Orlock, Associate Professor of Dance at Kansas State University, Faculty of the School for Body-Mind Centering, for her refined movement sense, invaluable insights, finely articulated ideas, and somatic editing of the manuscript; Dianne Woodruff, Ph.D., Registered Movement Therapist (ISMETA), for her perceptive suggestions and critical analysis of the material; and Dr. Thomas Verny, whose decades of work is at the forefront of the field in facilitating babies' psychology and health, for his enthusiastic support. Special thanks go to my husband, psychologist Dr. Louis Stokes, whose professional expertise was instrumental in making vital connections in the significant areas of movement, emotions, and cognitive development—our dialogues continue to be a lively, ongoing inspiration.

In particular, I would like to thank the professionals whose boundless enthusiasm and skilled expertise are visible in the vivid, expressive format of my book: Laura Bonazzali, developmental editor, for her concise questions and intelligent editing of these ideas from copious pages into a defining structure that makes the book user-friendly for parents; Karen Martin, illustrator, for her wonderfully accurate and universally appealing illustrations of the babies that so eloquently convey a clearer understanding of the essential movements developing in the first year; Cheryl Jordan, martial arts instructor and movement educator, for her willingness and proficiency in crafting the movement explorations with me that are so finely articulated in the photographs; Melanie Scott for her photographs that depict the dynamic movement sequences so effectively presented; Marina Bieler for her refined polishing of words; Malcolm Lester for his expertise in the publishing field; and Andrea Knight for her detailed copyediting and accomplished judgement in the final revisions that brought this book to fruition.

Acknowledgements

If you judge a book by its cover, it is a discerning photographer, Anne Jane Grieve, who has captured the dynamic energy of this book in her cover photos. My gratitude to Pronk&Associates, whose team effort has made this book a reality—their visually appealing design has made this book easily accessible and a joy to read and look at. Credit goes to Gord Pronk, Rudy Pietrolungo, Lisa Finlayson, Chandra Ganegoda, Francis Cowan, and Lynda Van Vroenhoven, who helped shape my vision and brought a professional commitment and friendly vitality that made the ongoing process a meaningful and rewarding experience.

Thanks to my son, Jason Stokes, for creating the numerous CDs of the video images. I am grateful to all of the above and to my family and many friends who listened attentively and are remembered for their ongoing support, ideas, and opinions during the writing and creation of this book.

Over the past decade, revolutionary discoveries in brain science and birth psychology have dramatically changed long-held theories of early development. The news, from world-class infant development research centers at Yale, Princeton, Rockefeller University, and elsewhere, is breathtaking in scope. Starting from the moment of conception, it turns out, a child's brain is wired by his environment, which at this point is, of course, his mother. Interaction with the environment is not merely one aspect of brain development, as had been thought; it is an absolute requirement, built into the process from our earliest days in the womb.

In this new paradigm, experiences prior to age three largely determine the architecture of the brain and the nature and extent of adult capacities; a secure relationship with a primary caregiver leads to more rapid acquisition of emotional and cognitive skills. Such interactions confer permanent advantages because they are evolution's number one tool for constructing the brain. Naturally, what I say here about the brain applies equally to the rest of the body.

The new brain science has disproved the notion that learning is more or less constant through the first three years of life. Instead, brain scans tell us that learning is actually explosive, occurring as different regions of the brain fire up, on schedule, for acquisition of specific skills, from language to music to math. Augment your child's experiences when the learning window for that skill is open and he will learn it well; miss it, and the skill will be much more difficult to acquire later.

The realization that genetics is not destiny and that environment is paramount to development carries a new opportunity for parents. Those physiological acts of a mother stroking her baby or a father playing with his daughter or son will be instantly converted to neurohormonal processes that transform the body and wire the brain of the child.

The latest research shows a baby's brain is literally tuned by her caregiver's brain to produce the correct neurotransmitters and hormones in the appropriate sequence; this entrainment determines, to a large degree, the brain architecture the child will have throughout life. If the tuning process is incomplete or inappropriate, it may damage the circuits of the prefrontal cortex, the seat of our most advanced human functions, producing an enduring vulnerability to psychological problems. But if the entrainment is appropriate, the child will be wired for health.

Infant development researchers around the world are discovering that the newborn's sensory systems are operational from birth, able to inform him of and relate to his surroundings. Because his expressive faculties, including his voice, facial muscles, and movements, are also well under control, a newborn baby is far more discriminating and communicative than was previously believed.

Indeed, over the past two decades, scientists have conducted thousands of studies on the sensory capabilities of the newborn, in the process rewriting the textbook on infant psychology and behavioral pediatrics. Viewed in aggregate, the research has established that the normal newborn enters the world with all their sensory systems functioning and intact. While each sense is developed to a different degree, they have *all* been documented as functioning in response to stimuli. By measuring such responses as leg withdrawal, head-turn, startle behavior, or eye blink, researchers have shown the extent of sensory development at each developmental stage.

Newborns are not only able to take in and interpret light and sound, odor, and taste, they can also perceive emotional nuance to a profound degree. Very young infants gaze at the faces of adults and respond in a way that seems tuned to the vocalizations and gestures of the adults. They smile when adults smile and move in rhythm to them. When the infant's predictions about the other person's response are ignored, for example, when the mother reacts to her baby's cooing with a perfectly still, non-emotional face, the baby becomes distinctly distressed.

The flow of love between mother and infant is as palpable an emotion as one can feel; the bond formed in the first critical days and weeks of a child's life will become a wellspring of love and caring for the baby and parents throughout their lives. Bonding is a dialogue, a dance between child and parent that starts before birth but comes into full bloom in the first few weeks and months of life after birth. To enhance bonding, there must be extended periods of contact between the mother, the father, and the baby in which they become intimate and connected with each other.

As a mother or father engages with their child, they enter an organized dialogue in which both partners, parent and baby, match emotional states and adjust their social attention to each other's signals. By setting her brain to the rhythms of her mother's brain, the baby ultimately learns the art of self-regulation; in other words, these early lessons enable the child, in future years, to rejoice in as well as master her emotional self.

It is the success of this process that propels babies to venture out from mother's familiar orbit to the novelty of the world. Indeed, the emotionally responsive parent creates a secure base from which the mobile baby and toddler can explore. To accomplish this, the child uses the parent's facial expression as a guide. Is it dangerous out there? Is it okay to roam? Mother's or father's face provides the answer. If the mood is positive, the dynamic generates high levels of energy, instilling in the infant the sense of elation necessary for play and exploration; these behaviors, in turn, lead to creation of novel situations that promote learning and the growth of the brain.

Beverly Stokes' book is based on a thorough understanding of these fundamental premises of child development. Building on these, she discusses in detail how the young child's exploration of his environment affects the development of his inner environment—in other words, the essential role body movement plays in developing body awareness and body image. Emerging from this dynamic foundation is the development of the baby's functional skills and his expressive, preverbal communication skills.

But there is much more. Parents who avail themselves of the book's wide range of experiential exercises will enhance the bonding process as well as facilitate their baby's natural progression of movement development. Through these exercises, parents will develop their agility, spontaneity, and nonverbal communication skills to fully enjoy their play sessions.

Beverly clearly demonstrates that the babies are self-directed learners when they engage in age-appropriate activities, and complete their own play sessions leading them from motivation to mastery. Babies also arrive at their own solutions when they set up their own action plans and problem-solving activities. Through the use of video vignettes, parents will be able to follow the entire sequence of an experiential episode—a very dynamic approach to learning.

The child who has established a healthy relationship to one or more loving adults has learned life's most valued lessons: how to feel feeling and how to self-reflect. These two traits are at the heart of empathic development. They are key to the capacity for compassion, joy, sadness, and love. The healthy child has also learned flexibility, the capacity to take in a complex array of internal and external information, sort through it, and make responses that are not merely reflexive and impulsive but reasoned.

Parents who read this book will learn that they can make a difference in their baby's development by

- being attentive when observing their baby,
- actively listening and responding to their preverbal cues, and
- participating in experiential exercises at the baby's level.

Child care professionals and educators will benefit by learning the body-mind organization overview and the relationship between movement and preverbal development. Based on this information they will discover new ways to observe, relate, and design activities for babies. Both these groups will find the material theoretically sound and of great practical value.

Thomas R. Verny, M.D., D. Psych., FRCPC.

Dr. Thomas Verny, author of the best-selling book, *The Secret Life of the Unborn Child,* is the founding president of the Association for Prenatal and Perinatal Psychology and Health and the founding editor of the *Journal of Prenatal and Perinatal Psychology and Health.*

A Developmental Movement Framework

This book is designed to provide you with a dynamic developmental movement framework for relating to your amazing baby in new ways. Using this framework, you will expand your observation skills to understand how babies move to learn, communicate, and interact in their environment. You will learn about the two major levels of development: pre-locomotion and locomotion. Within each level, there is a general sequence to a baby's movement development, but that sequence is not linear. Rather, the basic movement patterns progress in overlapping sequences—as one pattern is evolving, another new movement sequence is simultaneously emerging.

One-month-old baby.

There are also adult movement explorations in each chapter and the basic movement patterns are described in text and graphics to make them easy for you to do. These illustrated patterns will give you a better understanding of the movement process your baby is engaged in each month. Through your active participation, you will discover how this movement progression directly influences the development of

- the way your baby organizes her *body awareness* and *body image*,
- your baby's ability to be an *active participant* in social interaction,
- your baby's capacity to be a *self-motivated learner* in play.

With this knowledge, you will be able to create a receptive environment that encourages your baby's developing body awareness and her movement explorations.

One-year-old.

1

In the pre-locomotion stage, babies practice a variety of subtle body movements to develop their tactile body awareness and movement coordination. With all their senses actively engaged in both searching out new experiences and experimenting with their bodies, babies gradually discover that they can do what they intend to do. When babies are supported in their development as self-directed learners, they create their own action plans and problem-solving activities progressing from motivation to self-mastery.

Babies who are unable to do their own exploring, investigating, and discovering are at a serious disadvantage in their developing body psychology, which affects both their social interactions and their desire to learn in this crucial first year of development. It has become common knowledge that the sequence of brain development is genetically programmed but, as neurobiologists emphasize, it is the child's experiences that shape the quality of neural development.

Body movement is the essential ingredient needed for babies to develop a healthy body image, to explore their environment, and to build self-confidence through their successful play interactions. To enhance your baby's development you will learn to provide age-appropriate activities. As your baby engages in these activities, her natural curiosity and exploring nature take over so that, moving from motivation to mastery, she follows an activity through from the beginning to the end, making her own discoveries and arriving at her own solutions. These kinds of experiences provide the primary foundation on which your child builds her success as an active participant in social interaction and as a self-motivated learner preparing to enter the social world of preschool and elementary school.

Movement development in the first year of life has been my professional focus since 1985, when I began my longitudinal video studies of the baby's movements in a natural environment. Based on the comprehensive movement analyses of my extensive infant video

Two eight-month-old babies take turns using gestures, movement, and looking to communicate.

2

documentation, I have selected the video vignettes for this book that best reveal the baby's amazing movement development, parent-baby and peer interactions, and problem-solving episodes. By sharing these with you throughout this book, you will learn how to discover similar experiences as you participate in your baby's first year. The video vignettes have been selected from my video *Amazing Babies®: Moving in the First Year* and additional footage.

Your Unique Baby

Throughout this book, I emphasize the uniqueness of each baby. Although my intent is to provide an experiential guide to the average amount and quality of learning that takes place during each month, no baby is average. Each child develops in tune with his or her own rhythm and timing. If, for example, one baby has just turned four months and another baby is about to turn five months, the information provided in Chapter 4, "Moving from Motivation to Mastery," may not fully apply to the younger baby. Building on your attentive observation skills, you will come to recognize what is appropriate for your baby—creating new opportunities for her explorations and making informed choices at each stage of her development.

Move with Me

As you make your way through this book, you and your baby will embark on an experiential journey to explore a sequence of developmental movement patterns. The experiential exercises are designed for you to do, so that you can better relate to your baby's movement language. They are based on your baby's natural movement development in the first year. Your baby will explore these movement sequences spontaneously when you set up the appropriate environments for the pre-locomotion and the locomotion stages. You will learn to be at her perceptual and physical level on the floor and to be attentive to what your baby is doing at each stage; then you will observe and practice your baby's essential movements month by month, using this book as a guide.

A new father enjoys this body-to-body contact with his one-month-old baby.

3

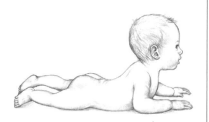

Baby at four months, supported on forearms.

You will readily recognize that the movement sequences you practice form the foundation of our adult movement repertoire. We constantly use these fundamental patterns in our daily activities, from rolling out of bed in the morning, to creeping under a table to get a toy, to reaching for an object on a high shelf, and to squatting down to communicate at eye level with a toddler. Indeed, body-movement re-education, yoga, and osteoporosis-reduction and back-care programs integrate into their activities the fundamental movements we experience during the first year of life.

Through your movement explorations, both you and your baby will experience a wide range of physical, emotional, and cognitive benefits. You, the parent (or caregiver), will

- develop your body awareness, improve your postural alignment, and move with greater agility,
- interact more spontaneously and freely in the way you hold, handle, and play with your baby,
- feel revitalized with renewed zest because of your active involvement,
- experience increased confidence as a parent,
- appreciate where your baby is developmentally at each stage.

4

Your baby will
- develop body-confidence because she is interacting with and learning about gravity,
- be content at her appropriate developmental level on the floor because you are also exploring the same movements,
- actively initiate her own play sessions because you give her time to problem solve,
- take the lead in social interactions because you are attentive and ready to play.

Learning Together

By learning along with your baby, you will activate your ability to improvise new movement games and adventures. Moreover, this movement foundation will help prepare you physically for the action-packed years to come, years filled with chase and catch games, running and jumping, action songs, dancing, playing sports, swimming, and simply having fun together. Grandparents will also benefit from this program because many of these exercises develop strength and provide joint stimulation. These movements will keep them limber and flexible and improve their balance and coordination. When older adults develop a renewed ease in changing levels from lying on the floor to hands and knees, to standing, they will certainly have a more enjoyable time interacting with their grandchildren, who are dynamic, energetic movers.

While you are adding one or two new experiential explorations each month, remember that your baby is practicing and building her own movement vocabulary day by day. The physical gains your baby is making through each new body awareness exploration and movement sequence expands her capabilities for discovery and play. By being attentive and moving with your baby, you develop a deep appreciation for her remarkable, unfolding accomplishments during this dynamic first year of life.

Following the sound of her mother's snapping fingers.

Face-to-face interaction.

Partners in Play

In each chapter, you will find a number of social interactions appropriate to each stage of your baby's development. By exploring these activities with your baby, you will enhance his developing

- body awareness and body image,
- movement coordination,
- balance and equilibrium,
- social interaction,
- expressive communication.

Most of these interactions take place at your baby's level on the floor. However, you might include several activities during care-giving times. For example, the body awareness game could be done at the diapering table with the adult standing. In the earliest months, you will usually engage your baby in playful body-to-body interactions while she is in your arms as well as when you are on the floor at your baby's level. The FloorPlay interactions support and enhance your baby's natural developmental movement process. Through such social games, you will become aware that babies are self-initiated learners and active participants in social interactions. Let your baby take the lead in social games, and you will discover you have an active partner in play!

Discovering the World of Movement

Movement is both *functional* and *expressive*. You can observe the functional aspect of movement in the way your baby performs a desired action—for example, when your baby comes to independent sitting or creeps to get a toy. *Functional* movement includes a baby's motor development and learning skills. You can observe *expressive* movement in your baby's body language during social interactions. Notice that the two aspects are not mutually exclusive. Your baby can accomplish his objective of pushing away a spoonful of spinach with a gesture that communicates exactly how he feels!

Body posture and gesture communicate confidence and interest.

6

By navigating the world through movement together, you'll become better and better at translating your baby's body language. In the pre-locomotion stage, your baby's body cues are subtle, but you will learn to recognize the little signals and vocalizations that tell you what he is saying. During the next six months, in the dynamic locomotion stage, babies become active explorers in their environment—your baby will advance to independent sitting, freeing his arms and hands to use expressive body postures, gestures, and babbling to communicate his intentions. You will learn that, from infancy on, our expressive body language and vocal tone are deeply rooted in our verbal messages.

Knowing through Experiencing

If you only read the following chapters, you will learn a great deal about your baby's development. But if you also explore the exercises, you will reach a new understanding of how your baby's body movement directly influences his body-confidence, social interactions, and problem-solving abilities each month. This experience gives you a tremendous advantage in guiding your baby's learning.

Parents, grandparents, and other caregivers who do the movement explorations in this book, rather than just reading about them, will gain increased confidence as they see the far-reaching effects of this experiential approach to parenting. When we begin to see babies as moving scientists, expansive explorers, eager investigators, delightful communicators, and improvisers in play, we can experience the joy of each unfolding moment from a new perspective.

Creating a Receptive Environment

A receptive environment will encourage you and your baby to move, explore, and interact spontaneously. Here are some tips for creating this environment:

Choose a time that is good for your baby, when she is rested, dry, fed, and alert.

In supported play, a five-month-old flings a soft toy down to the floor and picks it up again.

7

Warm and free to move, a four-month-old swims on her tummy.

Make sure that your baby

- is warm and free to move (flexible clothing, bare feet),
- has ample space to move freely at each stage,
- is on a padded floor (a carpet with a clean cover),
- has the option of a smooth floor for the symmetrical push pattern (wood or vinyl, not ceramic),
- has options for climbing (for older babies).

The time you choose should also be good for you. Your play sessions with your baby work best when you are relaxed and not thinking about being in two places at the same time. Allow yourself at least 20 minutes a day when you can be fully present with your baby.

You are

- at the baby's level (on the floor or ground),
- observing your baby attentively,
- aware that your baby's explorations are important to him (pause before you interact),
- ready for spontaneous action and interaction.

Let's talk a bit about each of the previous suggestions and why they are important.

FloorPlay

Place your baby on the floor and lie next to him where he can see you. Here, your baby is safe to engage in explorations in a variety of positions—lying on his back, belly, or side depending on his age, his stage of development, and the type of exploration he desires. When you provide your baby with enough floor space to play, he can initiate his own movement exploration, making significant discoveries at each stage. When you are at his level, he will be content to be on the floor, too. When he has completed an exploration, he may look up, wanting to play with you, and you will be right there, ready to join in one of his many spontaneous play interactions.

In the pre-locomotion stage (birth to five months), a carpeted floor offers the advantage of being able to support your baby's body without the risk of slipping. A carpeted floor is also best when babies are first learning to creep on their hands and knees around seven months of age. On the other hand, a smooth floor allows a six-month-old to push himself so that his whole body slides backward. When your baby is seven or eight months old, he might be ready to explore climbing. You can facilitate this exploration by sitting on the floor with your legs in the open V-position, so he can climb up and over your legs. When you are lying on your side on the floor, your baby can use your body to pull himself up to a kneeling position.

Observe Your Baby Attentively

While observing your baby, actively focus on what she is doing. She will be very aware of your presence, although she may not look at you directly until she completes her exploration. By observing attentively, you will know when your baby is ready for a change of pace or wants to play. Attention sometimes requires patience. Soon you will learn that your four-month-old baby's discovery of a new movement, a new vocalization, or a new way to turn a toy may lead to a focused 5-, 10-, or 15-minute exploration.

Pause before Interacting

In self-initiated play, babies are motivated by their own curiosity, interests, and desires to explore their environment. In open-ended play sessions, babies choose age-appropriate explorations that develop their body awareness and functional skills. They can set up their

In prone, a six-month-old develops her handling skills, and looks up to share her mastery.

own action plans, goals, and problem-solving activities. In successful interactions, babies explore at their own pace, complete their activities in their own time, and take pleasure in their self-mastery. Interrupting your baby during her explorations can frustrate her innate desire to learn.

Some parents, because they don't recognize that what their baby is doing is important, may be too eager to interact socially and interrupt their baby's play sessions. If they develop the habit of jumping in too quickly, especially during the early stages, they can adversely affect their baby's attention span and inhibit her initiative for learning. Recurring interruption prevents your baby's successful follow-through of an action from start to finish. This may lead to frustration and lack of enthusiasm, which will affect your baby's ability to concentrate on what interests her.

Remember when you were first learning how to ride a bicycle? You had to concentrate on every little part of the process: balance, endurance, coordination, timing, and spatial awareness. Then, you had to put it all together. Initially, you could stay upright on your bike for only a few feet. But within days, you could ride around the block by yourself. What a feeling of mastery!

Mastering a new skill requires
- *curiosity and interest*
- *exploration*
- *time to problem solve*
- *pleasure in practice*

Be Spontaneous

Spontaneity means being ready to improvise in the moment. But your ability to improvise appropriately for the developmental level of your baby stems from your knowledge of and your experience with your baby. When you observe your baby attentively and develop your awareness through your own movement explorations, you increase the depth of your understanding so that you respond appropriately to your baby's cues. In the pre-locomotion stage, when your three-month-old reaches out to you with both hands, you are there with a soft toy he can pull or tug. When your five-month-old rolls over to look at you and reaches out with one hand to touch your face, you move closer to feel his loving touch. When a toy rolls out of your baby's reach, you move it toward him so he can continue his explorations.

All babies need to be successful in their interactions. There is value in letting your baby play on his own, trusting in his natural ability to solve the problems he sets for himself. Because you are tuned in, you know when to intervene. When you interact with your baby spontaneously, you can choose different responses to different situations as they evolve. For example, when your baby is at the beginning stages of creeping on hands and knees but hasn't mastered the action yet, you may choose to entice him with a toy, just out of reach, to encourage him to creep toward you. It is important not to overdo this—let him learn to coordinate his body so that he can creep on his own. If your baby is getting overly frustrated, move the toy closer to him so that he can successfully grasp it. Be patient, soon he will be creeping and able to reach things on his own. By that time, you will have learned how to create a physically safe environment so that your new explorer can go where he wants and get what he wants. It is important for babies to play on their own for uninterrupted periods of time each day so they can follow their desires and carry out their intentions to complete their play activities. Confidence, pleasure in learning, and self-esteem result when babies initiate, follow through, and complete their activities—"from motivation to self-mastery"!

Following your baby's lead in bear walking.

11

Special Features of This Book

Adult Movement Explorations

As you follow your baby's movement development, each new body sequence invites an opportunity to deepen your understanding of your own body-mind integration through the *Adult Movement Explorations*. Since these early developmental movement patterns underlie all adult movement, you will learn how to coordinate your body in new ways and expand your functional and expressive movement repertoire. Movement that is graceful, efficient, and effortless leaves you feeling energized and refreshed. Your newfound body ease will flow into other areas of your life and you may begin to notice that you are more spontaneous in communication. Most importantly, you will be more playful in social interactions with your baby.

Parent-Baby Interactions

Throughout the book, you will notice a section called *Parent-Baby Interactions*. These face-to-face and body-to-body activities, especially in the earlier months, provide you with some suggestions to try with your baby. They are a wonderful way to encourage communication and social interaction. Later on, your parent-baby interactions will spontaneously flow from your FloorPlay explorations. You will also find sound and vocalizing games that are fun to do together.

In Your Journal

At the end of the chapter, look for a page called *In Your Journal*. Each month some relevant questions are posed to assist you in documenting your movement explorations and what you also observed in your baby's developing movement, communication, and learning.

Highlights

Each chapter closes with the *Highlights* of the month. This page will serve as a quick reminder for you of all the things your baby explored and learned during the month.

Benefits for parents, grandparents, and caregivers

- *developing a new understanding of how babies move*
- *enriching play and social interactions with your baby*
- *enhancing your own body-mind integration*

Supported standing in FloorPlay.

12

Relating to your budding toddler.

Your Active Participation

What I envision for the parent, as well as grandparent, caregiver, child-care professional, and educator, is participation in a new approach to parenting based on your active physical involvement. Learning through the experience of movement will make you more aware of your baby's subtle movement development, communication cues, and problem-solving skills. The more you participate, the deeper your appreciation will be of her increasingly competent abilities. The first year with your baby will be a unique journey because of the receptive environment that you provide. From this foundation that encourages freedom of movement and exploration, your baby will show you her unique abilities and amazing accomplishments. With this book beside you as your guide, you are about to participate in a year of treasured experiences with *your amazing baby.*

Pre-Locomotion Stage

Newborn To Five Months

During the first half-year of your baby's life, she will undergo a dramatic change from lying in a self-contained place, defined by the reach of her arms and legs, to acquiring the ability to move herself from one place to another. Underlying her incredible transformation in the pre-locomotion stage, are three key achievements:

- learning to move and interact with the force of gravity,
- developing a greater awareness of her body and its boundaries,
- establishing her body image (which you will recognize as she progresses through four basic patterns of movement).

This is the movement foundation that gets the developmental ball rolling in preparation for the dynamic locomotion stage, starting at approximately six months. Let's look at each of these three key achievements of the first half-year in a bit more depth.

Mastering Gravity:
Developing a Secure Relationship to the Earth

Weightlessness in space travel contributes to loss of bone density and muscle strength and leads to disorientation in equilibrium. Knowing this helps us appreciate the importance of a baby's relationship to gravity and the influence of gravity on his physical movement and social development. When your baby emerges from his watery womb environment, he feels supported by the earth's friendly force of gravity and knows where he is in space. This sense of security enhances all his other relationships. In her book, *Sensory Integration and the Child,* Jean Ayres states, "Gravitational security is so vital to emotional

Newborn baby.

Five-month-old.

15

health that nature has given us a strong inner drive to explore gravity and master it."

Your baby's learning begins with gravity and his body. While your baby is lying on his stomach and lifting his head or pushing against the floor with his forearms, he is exploring gravity, its pull on his body, and his ability to move against the pull of gravity. Your baby's relationship to gravity is primary to his security, comfort, growth, and development. It is essential that babies bond to the earth's pull so that they can rest, allowing their bodies to yield to the force of gravity. Bonnie Bainbridge Cohen, in her integrated approach to movement, coins the action terms "yield and push in relationship to gravity." In her book, *Sensing, Feeling, and Action,* she emphasizes that our basic postural tone (that is, the readiness of the muscles to respond) is an indication of how we are relating to gravity and is reflected in our movement, "Low tone indicates that we are having difficulty meeting the force of the earth's pull; high tone indicates that we are overreacting to the pull of gravity; an even, balanced tone indicates that we have a comfortable relationship or balance with the earth's force." When babies learn to interact with gravity first by yielding and then by pushing, they develop balanced tone as a foundation for future movement explorations.

Body Awareness:
Developing a Sense of the Body's Boundaries

Babies thrive on the loving touches they receive from their parents. It is common knowledge that touching, holding, and cuddling are necessary to every baby's sense of body comfort and healthy emotional development. But how do babies learn "where they begin and where they end?" In other words, how do babies embody themselves? You will learn to observe how babies embody themselves through their own physical movement, touch, and body-to-body contact.

The close link between your baby's body movement, specific tactile sensations, and visual processing informs her about herself from the beginning. We see the baby's early developing body awareness when she touches her head with her hand—and her eyes move in the direction of the felt touch. During the pre-locomotion stage, babies participate in a variety of body contact explorations such as hand-to-head, mouth-to-hand, hand-to-mouth, hand-to-hand, foot-to-foot, hands-to-knees, ankle-to-ankle, hands-to-feet, feet-to-mouth, and two-hands-on-one-foot. These antigravity movements and body-to-body explorations are fundamental to the way that babies embody themselves. With these self-initiated movement explorations, your baby develops her awareness of her body and her body's boundaries, learning where each individual part of her body is and how it is moving in relation to another part of her body. In the pre-locomotion stage, your baby's body awareness explorations take place in a contained space defined by the reach of her arms and legs.

The following tactile explorations are common to most babies in the *supine* position (lying on the back).

3 months *(hand-to-hand)*
This three-month-old brings her hands to her chest and clasps them together. Her legs assume the frog-leg posture.

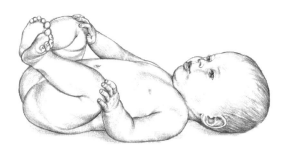

4 months *(hands-to-knees)*

This four-month-old progresses from the frog-leg posture to raising her knees higher and reaches down to hold on to her knees.

5 months *(hands-to-feet)*

This five-month-old holds on to her feet without rolling and can bring her toes to her mouth. She can cross her midline and grasp one foot with two hands.

From the above examples, you can readily see the changes that occur in the *supine* position over a few months. Babies also develop their body awareness in *prone* (lying on the front); for example, a four-month-old clasps her hands together. Body awareness also develops in *side lying* (lying on each side); for example, a five-month-old brings her hands together, hands-to-knees and hands-to-feet.

You will learn to recognize the importance of these movement and tactile explorations to her developing body awareness in the pre-locomotion stage.

18

Body Image:
Developing the Four Basic Movement Patterns

As you follow the movements through which your baby progresses during the first year of life—first lifting her head, then crawling, sitting, creeping, standing, and walking—you will learn to recognize four basic organizing patterns that underlie these movements.

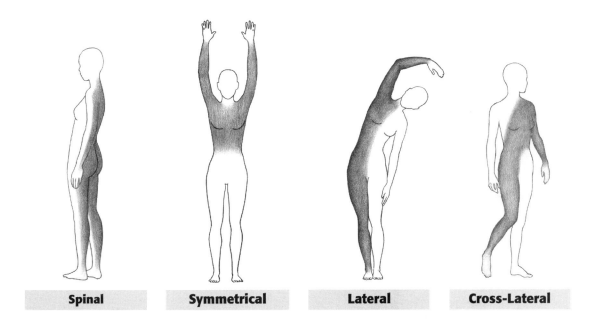

| **Spinal** | **Symmetrical** | **Lateral** | **Cross-Lateral** |

1. **Spinal Movement Patterns**
   – head-to-tail: extension, flexion, lateral flexion, and rotation

2. **Symmetrical Movement Patterns**
   – both arms and/or both legs together

3. **Lateral Movement Patterns**
   – each arm and leg on the same side of the body together

4. **Cross-Lateral Movement Patterns**
   – right arm/left leg together and left arm/right leg together

Bonnie Cohen explains that inherent in each of the developmental movement patterns is the combination of two or more of the following actions—*yielding, pushing, reaching,* and *pulling.*

Yield and Push are patterns of *compression* that develop through one's relationship to *gravity.* In these patterns, babies yield to connect with the force of gravity and develop strength by pushing their whole body weight against the resistance of gravity.

Reach and Pull are patterns of *elongation* that develop through one's relationship to *space.* In these patterns, babies focus and reach outward, developing streamlined mobility and lightness to change body levels and explore new frontiers of space in their environment.

The strength and support of the *Yield and Push Patterns* precede the articulate lightness and agility of the *Reach and Pull Patterns.* Therefore, in independent movement, the stability of support precedes the mobility of the limbs. As your baby progresses through a series of developmental movement patterns, she is also establishing and differentiating her body image and sense of physical identity. The differentiation and coordination of the body can be organized into these four patterns.

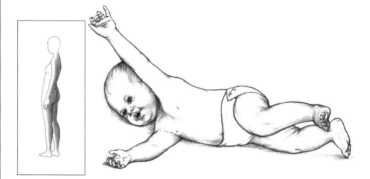

1. **Spinal Movement Patterns** differentiate the front of the body from the back of the body.

20

2. **Symmetrical Movement Patterns** differentiate the upper body from the lower body.

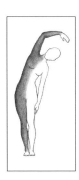

3. **Lateral Movement Patterns** differentiate the right side from the left side of the body.

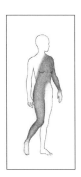
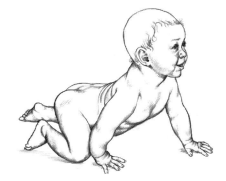

4. **Cross-Lateral Movement Patterns** differentiate the diagonal pathway from the right arm to the left leg and from the left arm to the right leg.

21

The Introduction and Part One provide you with the movement framework in text, visual, and graphic format so that you can better understand the essential patterns of movement your baby is forming in this remarkable first year, the foundation for our adult movement repertoire. As you read through this book, you will discover more about how these developmental movement patterns emerge, evolve, and relate to each other. It is through your movement explorations that you will be inspired to provide your baby with a supportive environment that communicates to her that you value her fundamental learning experiences. When your baby is content to be at her level of experience and learning, she can focus on her explorations and calmly complete them from motivation to mastery.

Beginning a Developmental Journey Together

Now you are ready to embark on a most engaging journey with your baby in a receptive environment that you provide. The importance of moving your body and playing with your baby on the floor cannot be emphasized enough. Keep a "beginner's mind"—you have an enthusiastic teacher in your baby. As you observe her movements unfold, she can show you her diligent practice, revealing how accomplished she is at doing these complex, sophisticated developmental movements in their natural sequence and in her own timing. These are the essential movements your baby is doing naturally, when you provide her with enough time and space to move freely. Set time aside, between 20 and 30 minutes each day, when you can be fully engaged in your baby's FloorPlay sessions. You are learners together. Make these times convenient for you, so that you enjoy every moment.

The video vignettes identified in the Introduction describe different babies' preverbal experiences during each month. To refine your observation skills, you may want to study the frame by frame presentation first and write down what you recognize before reading the vignette description and interpretation. Let the babies in this book's many vignettes show you how they move, communicate, and learn. From your study, you will be more tuned-in to your baby as she develops her exquisite movement, subtle communication, and successful problem-solving skills.

Observe, listen, and learn from your baby's experiences, as each new exploration captures his attention. Wait until your baby sends you a little cue, maybe a special look, gesture, or vocalization, that says he wants you to participate. In this way, you are letting him know you are enjoying what he is doing, and letting him take the lead in your social interactions. These joyful explorations and interactions happen at your baby's level, on the floor where "his world" is unfolding.

One of the best ways to be in tune with yourself is through body movement. Do all the explorations at your own pace, and learn to be attentive to your individual requirements for rest and recuperation. You will notice the breathing and movement explorations I have put in Chapters 1, 2, and 3 are a gentle and subtle way to begin listening to your body. By exploring the developmental movements that your baby is doing, you will learn how her play time provides the necessary formative experiences that facilitate her growth and development.

Now let's begin to learn about your baby's dance of development—how she moves, communicates, and learns in her own unique way, right from the first month!

Born to Move

One Month

Cuddling your baby in your arms, you gaze attentively at his face and notice that he is looking just as intently at you. His ability to actively focus on your face provides a clue to the development of your baby's visual attention. By following your animated facial expressions, your baby is using his eyes as information gatherers. This early experience shows the baby's visual recognition of his parents. Your new baby is curious and all his visual experiences contribute to his learning. Even though a newborn notices some colors, it has been well documented that babies are more sensitive to light and dark contrasts, preferring sharp outlines and black and white patterns.

In this chapter, we will explore your baby's earliest adventures in movement. Babies tune in to things that move, and they respond right from the beginning by mimicking your movement. This may begin when she gazes at your changing facial expressions or when she sees your tongue move in a to-and-fro motion in and out of your mouth. People and things that move toward her and then move away from her seem to capture her attention.

The baby's interaction with the world thus promotes the growth of his brain, which in turn enhances his ability to experience and understand his environment.

— Stanley Greenspan,
Building Healthy Minds

25

One day, you may begin to notice that your baby sticks out her tongue or reaches out rather tentatively with one hand to grasp your finger. At this point, you may find it difficult to believe that within a few months your baby will reach out with both hands to touch your face and, by the end of the pre-locomotion stage, shift her weight to free one hand to reach out to touch you or to grasp toys and objects. But let's not move too quickly! The subtle changes over the next few weeks will amaze you.

Spinal Movement

When your baby was in the womb, her spine was shaped in a flexed C-curve. At one month, uncurling her arms and legs, she is already more extended than she was as a newborn. When lying on her back or belly, your baby can lift and turn her head to each side, and she usually lies with her head resting to one side.

At this age, when she lies on her belly your baby's spinal movement is like a seesaw: when her head comes up, her tail goes down; when her tail goes up, her head goes down.

Developing in close relationship to the earth's pull, your baby will progress from yielding to gravity to pushing away from the force of gravity. You will gain a new understanding of how your baby's learning begins with gravity and her body, and how each antigravity movement clarifies your baby's relationship to this force.

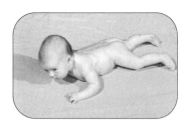
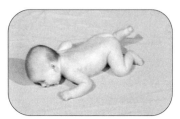

Spinal seesaw.

Adult Movement Explorations

Lying Down Semi-Supine

- Prepare a clean padded surface, such as an exercise mat or a carpeted floor.
- You may need a small square pillow or folded towel to support your head.
- Lie down on your back.
- Rest your arms comfortably at your sides with your palms up or down.

- Flex your knees, raise your legs one after the other, and place your feet flat on the floor.
- Place your feet under your knees, shoulder width apart.
- Yield to gravity and allow your body to be supported by the floor.
- In this semi-supine position, breathe easily for about ten minutes.

In supine, the one-month-old baby turns his head farther to the side.

Lying Down Prone

Whenever you lie down, yield to gravity and allow your body to be supported by the floor.

- Prepare a clean padded surface, such as an exercise mat or a carpeted floor.
- Lie down on your stomach with your head resting to the left.
- Place your arms in the primitive flexed position as shown in the following illustration.
- Keep your forearms in contact with the floor.

27

- Breathe easily and maintain this position briefly to notice the increased sense of weight or tone on the front of your body.
- We will expand this exploration in Chapter 2, Head Lifting and Turning.

In prone, the one-month-old baby rests with her head more rotated to the side.

Parent-Baby Interactions

Baby's Body Comfort in Prone

The best way to facilitate your baby's development in the prone position is by exploring the following exercise, which will help your baby communicate her body comfort level to you.

- Place your baby on her back, on a clean blanket or on a carpet or mat on the floor.
- Lie down on your back beside her.
- Flex your knees, raise your legs one after the other, and place your feet flat on the floor.
- Roll to your side and take your baby in your arms.
- Bring your baby to your chest and, holding her securely, carefully roll onto your back again.
- Adjust your feet so they are flat on the floor, shoulder width apart.
- In this semi-supine position, support your baby to rest in the prone position on your body.

This exercise will increase the muscle tone on the front surface of your baby's body and will facilitate her body comfort and development in the prone position.

Baby in prone, bonding with her father.

Note: babies should not be left unattended in the prone position.

28

Mouthing, Looking, and Handling

Your baby's lips and hands are exquisitely sensitive, having the largest number of touch receptors in the body. With their mouths, babies learn about the actions of reaching, grasping, releasing, and withdrawing from the nipple during feeding. At the same time, your baby is also gathering information as she gazes attentively at your face and holds on to your finger tightly with her hands (grasp reflex). Over the next few months, babies use mouthing and handling to explore toys and objects. Mouthing teaches babies about specific properties such as hardness and about the shapes of objects. Through their developing eye-hand coordination, babies grasp and investigate objects to learn more and discover new tactile information about their surroundings. These experiences are the foundation of your baby's ability to match what she sees with what she experiences by mouthing, touching, and handling.

Oral Rooting Reflex

You will notice the oral rooting reflex when you're feeding your baby. This reflex supports her ability to search for and find the nipple and turn her head from side to side. When you lightly stroke the area around your newborn's mouth, she will respond by turning her mouth toward the touch stimulation. This primitive reflex underlies rotation of the head.

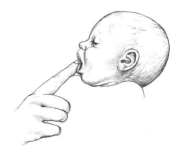

Stimulating the oral rooting reflex.

Parent-Baby Interactions

Breast-feeding

- Brush the corner of your baby's mouth so that she actively roots and turns her head to search for your breast.
- After you have nursed your baby on one side, explore this reflex while cradling your baby on the opposite side.

Your baby's vision is most acute at approximately the distance from your chest level to your face.

29

We don't often think to provide the same experience to a bottle-fed baby as we do to a breast-fed baby, that is, to alternate holding your baby in each arm and stimulate the rooting reflex from both directions. The following is especially important for fathers, grandparents, and other caregivers.

Bottle-feeding

It is important to hold your baby on both sides of your body.

- It is important to hold your baby when bottle-feeding.
- Brush the corner of your baby's mouth with the bottle's nipple, so that she actively searches for it.
- After you have fed your baby on one side, cradle her in your arms on the opposite side of your body.
- Stimulate this reflex again so that she turns her head to search for the bottle's nipple.
- In this way she experiences looking at you from both sides.

Adult Movement Explorations

Head Rotation

- Lie on the floor on your back with your knees flexed and your feet flat on the floor.
- Allow your body to yield to gravity.
- Breathe easily.
- Simply turn your head to the right and to the left.
- Do this a few times, noting the activation of the muscles of your neck.
- Now, with your right hand, brush the right corner of your mouth and follow the stimulation as your head rolls effortlessly in the direction of your touch.
- With your left hand, brush the left corner of your mouth and repeat the motion to the left.

As you pay attention to your sensation, you heighten your awareness so that you can release any excessive tension in and around your mouth, jaw, or throat. In adults, this is a major cause of facial and neck tension.

Variation

I have used this variation successfully with seniors who have lost the ability to rotate their heads in order to look behind, for example, when driving their car.

- Sit upright on a chair.
- Look over your right shoulder.
- Notice what you can see, at the farthest point.
- Return your head to center, your body's midline.
- Brush the corner of your mouth (rooting reflex).
- Look over your right shoulder at the same time.

Did your head rotate beyond what you could initially see?
- Repeat this exploration on the left side.

Social Interaction

Your baby's ability to interact with you grows and blossoms over the next few months. Each day, as you gaze at your baby, you notice a variety of new expressions flicker across her face, and one day you sense that her expression matches your own. Her capacity to communicate is based on these intimate interactions and mutual mirroring experiences.

We are all born with a unique voice and the need to be heard. Your newborn's voice announced her arrival loud and clear. Her first cry stimulates her breathing and communicates a potent message to "respond." This cry and your response are the essence of all vocalized call and response games in social interactions. This month, she listens and responds to your soothing voice, cooing and singing. By making different crying sounds, she is able to communicate her needs more specifically.

When we talk about body movement, we don't usually think of the movement of our tongue. Yet, it has been documented that babies can mimic an adult's tongue game from the first days of life. Because of the sucking instinct, babies develop tremendous control over their tongues. Engage your baby when she is quiet and alert.

Notice how easy it is to rotate your head by activating the oral rooting reflex.

31

Mimicking Tongue Vignette.

Mimicking Tongue Vignette

Mary Jo is looking at her mother's face. She notices her mother's tongue move in and out of her mouth. Concentrating on her mother's tongue, Mary Jo begins to move her tongue in her mouth and then she turns away. By turning her head away, Mary Jo communicates that she doesn't want to play this tongue game today. Her mother changes her body position and cuddles her in her arms.

Parent-Baby Interactions

Face-to-Face Tongue Wagging

- Hold your baby on your lap facing you.
- Support your baby's head and neck.
- Look at each other.
- Slowly move your tongue in and out of your mouth several times.
- Observe to see if your baby responds by moving her tongue.

Seeing you move your tongue in and out of your mouth resonates with your baby's experience of feeding and making sounds. Be sensitive to your baby's response, as she may not want to engage. Next month you may notice that your baby adds a smile to her tongue game, extending her social interaction with you.

Adult Breathing Explorations

The following breathing and sound explorations are developed from my work with Carl Stough, founder of the Institute of Breathing Coordination. Research has shown that most people use only a small fraction of their breathing potential. Restricted breathing decreases the flow of oxygen to the body. By breathing more efficiently, you will experience a new sense of well-being with improved zest and vitality. You will also become a more calming presence for your baby.

You will need
- a clean padded surface, such as an exercise mat or a carpeted floor,
- a small, thin, square pillow or folded towel for under your head,
- a regular-size pillow for under your knees.

The following exercises may reawaken internal sensations that increase feelings of vitality throughout your whole body.

Breathing Basics

- Lie down on the floor with your arms comfortably at your sides.
- Explore the freedom of your tongue.
- In your regular speaking voice, say *la-la-la*.
- Whisper *la-la-la*.
- Next, without making a sound, move your tongue to shape *la-la-la*.
- Notice as you do this that your breath flows out as you exhale.
- Place the palm of your hand in front of your mouth and feel the warmth of your breath.

It is essential to begin with an exhalation to experience your reflexive inhalation. You will notice that the length of your exhalation varies, perhaps as *la-la-la-la* or short *la-la* or longer *la-la-la-la-la-la*, depending on what point you begin to exhale after your reflexive inhalation.

Moving your tongue (*la-la*) keeps your throat open to extend your exhalation. You don't have to think about taking a big breath because inhaling is a reflexive response. Notice that inhaling through your mouth and nose is a natural response that occurs when making sounds, speaking, or singing.

33

Breathing: Book Experiment

- Lie down on the floor with your arms comfortably at your sides.
- Place a book on your abdomen. The book should be heavy enough for you to sense its weight.
- Allow your body to yield to gravity and rest.
- Silently move your tongue *la-la-la* as you exhale.
- The book on your abdomen slowly lowers with each exhalation.
- At the end of your exhalation, notice the reflexive inhalation.
- The book rises up with each reflexive inhalation.
- Do not push or hold your abdomen in or out in any way.
- With your mouth comfortably open, continue to explore your breathing, silently moving your tongue *la-la-la-la-la* to the end of each exhalation.
- Explore 3 complete breath cycles.

Book experiment

- *If you let out all the air at the beginning of the exercise, the book will lower quickly.*
- *If you force your breath in any way, the book will bounce up as the abdomen protrudes to support the sound. This indicates the diaphragm is not supporting the vocalized sound.*

Making Sounds

As you become more comfortable, you can add sound to your exploration. All forms of vocalized sounds—humming, singing, crying, and speaking—promote breathing by exercising the respiratory system.

- Use a sibilant *sss* (hissing sound) in place of silent *la-la-la*.
- When hissing, if you force the air out too quickly, you will feel out of breath at the end of the exercise.
- Use an *mmm* sound (humming sound).

The Spinal Wave

- Remove the pillow from under your knees.
- Assume the semi-supine position, lying on your back with your knees flexed and your feet flat on the floor.
- Play with finding the best place for your feet so they actively contact the floor.
- Check the vertical alignment of your body from head to tailbone.
- If you feel any stress in your neck, place a folded towel under your head.
- Place your arms comfortably at your sides, palms contacting the floor as shown in the drawings below.

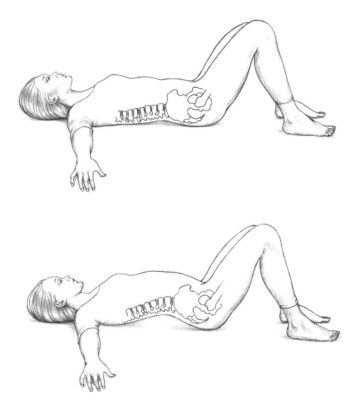

When you breathe, your entire spine subtly changes shape.

1. *Exhalation: your lumbar spine flattens; notice that your chin moves away from your chest.*

2. *Inhalation: your lumbar spine arches slightly; notice that your chin moves closer to your chest.*

In this exploration, do not press your back into the floor or arch your back away from the floor. The movement of your spine occurs in response to your breathing.

- Begin by exhaling and moving your tongue *la-la-la*.
- Bring your attention to your spine.
- Notice that your lumbar curve (lower back) flattens as you exhale.
- Notice a slight arch in your lumbar curve when you reflexively inhale.
- You may experience these undulating movements all the way to your tailbone.
- Notice how your breath moves your pelvis and creates a gentle rocking.
- Explore this spinal wave for three complete cycles.
- Increase your awareness all the way up your spine to notice the movement of your head.
- Exhale *la-la-la*.
- Notice that as your lumbar spine flattens during your exhalation, your chin moves away from your chest.
- When you reflexively inhale, your lumbar spine arches slightly and your chin moves toward your chest.
- Explore this spinal wave for three breathing cycles.

Holding the breath is one of the most common breathing problems. This often occurs when people are tense, concentrating, or trying to hear what someone is saying. For children and adults, the book experiment and simple activities such as blowing bubbles or sighing are all delightful explorations that will prolong the exhalation of breath. Making sounds and singing strengthen the diaphragm.

In Your Journal

Keep a journal about your breathing and movement explorations. Enjoy this time to tune in to yourself and you will be surprised at the many benefits you will experience over time. Listening to your body in this way may be new to you, so be patient. During each month, write down how the explorations add to your body awareness. In your "breathing with book" experiment, be attentive to yourself to ensure that your abdomen doesn't protrude during your exhalation or while making sounds.

You may want to keep a baby journal. During each month, jot down how your breathing and movement explorations fine-tune your observation skills with your baby. The following are a few questions you might ask yourself. How have these explorations enhanced the way you respond to your baby? Are you more aware of how you hold your baby and how you shape your body to each other? Are you moving gracefully and smoothly when you are holding your baby?

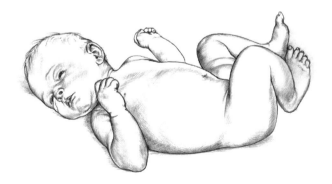

One-Month Highlights

Body Awareness
- Hand-to-mouth
- Discovering own tongue
- Mouthing hands

Movement Development and Learning
- Reflexes—rooting, Moro, and grasp
- Yielding to gravity
- Lifting and turning head in prone
- Spinal seesaw in prone
- Sensitive to high contrast patterns

Communication and Social Interactions
- Gazes at your face
- Responds to facial expressions
- Mimics tongue wagging
- Reaches to touch your face
- Listens to your voice
- Crying
- Enjoys body-to-body contact

Sensing and Feeling through Movement

2

Two Months

Your two-month-old baby is more alert, having greater sensory awareness. He is not just passively receiving stimulation; even at this early age, he can actively search out what he will focus on, pay attention to, and interact with. Babies learn about themselves and organize their experiences in relationship to a responsive environment. He now links up all forms of sensory information through his body movement.

Your baby's sense of touch is exquisite. As he coordinates his arm actions, he makes more connections between the things he feels, touches, and sees within his arm's reach and visual field. Even before birth, your baby's hearing was well developed. At two months, while resting with his head to one side, he can orient to a sound behind him. He can lift and turn his head toward the source of the sound and match what he sees with what he hears. Smiling, vocalizing, and turning both toward and away from stimulation are the preverbal cues that communicate his curiosity, pleasure, or frustration.

A healthy brain stimulates itself by active interaction with what it finds challenging and interesting in its environment.

— Jane Healy,
Endangered Minds

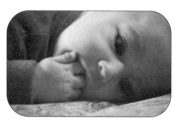

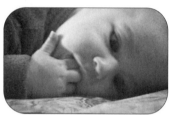

Hand-to-Mouth Vignette.

At two months, your baby has better control of his head and neck in prone. He can lift and turn his head in both directions with more ease. Toward the end of this month, your baby will have progressed to holding his head up 45°. He may briefly maintain his head in the center of his body, supporting himself on his forearms with fisted hands. This control of his head and neck enhances his developing visual control. Your baby also rests his head to one side when lying on his back. It will be several months before his neck muscles are developed enough so that he can lift his head up in midline to watch diapering activities or body games in supine.

Movement and Touch

At this age, your sensing, feeling, animated baby is interested in his body processes and in touching, looking, and listening. Let's follow Colm's hand-to-mouth exploration so that we can understand his world in more detail.

Hand-to-Mouth Vignette

Colm is lying in the prone position with his head turned to one side. He explores by bringing his hand to his mouth, extending and sliding his arm on the surface of the sofa, following his hand with his eyes. The novelty of Colm's experience—mouthing his hand, extending and flexing his arm, feeling the different textures he touches, and watching the movements he makes—provides him with a wide variety of new internal and external sensations. When he finishes exploring, he looks up and smiles to express his pleasure.

These successful hand-to-mouth explorations contribute to your baby's developing body awareness and also help him comfort and soothe himself. The activity of watching his hand move back and forth develops his eye-hand coordination.

Visual Tracking

Your baby's eyes are beginning to converge, to work together. When you place your baby on the floor to lie on her back and you hold a toy above her head, she can track the moving toy smoothly from her midline to the side and from the side to past her midline. You will notice that she can follow a toy horizontally with more awareness of the periphery. Her color vision continues to be refined during this month.

The best way for your baby to develop her visual sense is through moving her body. Developing good head and neck control in the prone position facilitates the development of your baby's visual control. The prone position also helps your baby develop her eye-hand coordination when she watches the movement of her hand in hand-to-mouth interactions.

Getting to Know You

During the first year, your shared interactions are often body-to-body. When you hold your baby, she picks up a variety of cues from you, including the focus of your attention, your hand and arm pressure, your breathing pattern, vocal tone, and expressive body actions. A baby quickly senses how you are feeling. She can tell if you're relaxed or rushed, delighted or annoyed, happy or upset. She doesn't have to put all the bits and pieces of you and your actions together. Instead, a synthesis of "you-ness" flows through your actions and interactions, which is what your baby responds to. It is the cohesiveness of your involvement in what you are doing and saying that conveys your authentic expression. Your nonverbal expression can begin with a hand gesture or head motion, but then it ripples through your whole body. Your baby perceives the whole picture in the harmony of your posture, gestures, and tone of voice. When these components are integrated, they create the feeling of "you."

Looks at and follows a small musical chime.

Animated face-to-face interaction.

Smiling

Your baby's expressive communication repertoire is expanding. In her daily interactions, it is still your lively face that captures her attention. During this month, you will be greeted with lots of smiles that spread through her whole body. Social smiling is one of the interactive expressions of a budding two-month-old baby. Babies smile in response to smiles, and can elicit smiles from others. Your social two-month-old may readily tag a smile on to the familiar tongue-wagging game, extending your social playtime. In her book, *Play,* Catherine Garvey points out that smiling and laughter are not only early forms of expression, but also important ways to both initiate and maintain communication exchanges.

Your baby's face-to-face interactions are really whole-body experiences. When babies and parents gaze and smile at each other, they respond with their whole bodies. When we smile, our breathing deepens and our bodies relax, expand, and lengthen. When we frown, our breathing becomes shallow, we tense up, and our bodies narrow and shorten. Now when your baby sees your animated face, she responds from head to toe, with a body wriggle and beaming face.

Mimicking Tongue Vignette.

Mimicking Tongue Vignette

Mara is gazing intently at her mother's face and her mother is gazing at her. Mara notices the movement of her mother's tongue. Her tongue seems to come out toward her and then moves away from her. After gazing intently at her mother's tongue appearing and disappearing, Mara starts moving her tongue in her mouth. Then, opening her mouth, she slides her tongue out between her lips, mimicking the movement of her mother's tongue. This month, Mara readily adds a smile to her tongue-wagging game.

When your baby extends her communication with you, by adding a smile to her tongue-wagging game, she is further developing her social skills.

Parent-Baby Interactions

Tongue Wagging Variation

- Wag your tongue up and down, touching your top lip and your bottom lip.
- Do this a few times. Notice his responses—both the movement of his eyes and his expression of interest.
- Move your tongue by sliding it from side to side a few times. Again observe his responses.

He may be more interested in the novelty you have added to the game than in doing the same movement. He may still move his tongue in and out of his mouth and add on a smile.

Watch for these preverbal cues:
- *Your baby may add a smile to this tongue-wagging game.*
- *When your baby turns away, perhaps he needs time to absorb his experience.*
- *See if your baby turns back to face you to continue.*
- *Babies will yawn, squirm, fuss, or cry to show they have had enough.*

Hearing

Hearing is well developed at birth and your baby can distinguish between all the sounds that make up his rich sonic environment—between familiar and new voices, pets, everyday sounds, music, and rattles. Much has been written about the importance of the mother's high-pitched voice to her baby, but it is the unique sound of your voice that is special to her. When you come into a room, she may smile just hearing the sound of your voice before she even sees you. Now that your baby can locate the direction and source of a sound, she can play auditory games with you, tracking your voice or a pleasant-sounding musical chime or toy.

43

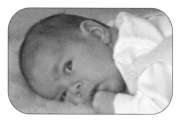

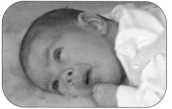

Musical Sound Vignette.

Musical Sound Vignette

Mara is lying down in the prone position. Her mother is sitting behind her and shakes a musical rattle. The sound captures Mara's attention. Her eyes synchronize to the rhythmic sound she hears. Searching for the sound, Mara's desire is to see what she hears. Mara lifts and turns her head in the direction of the sound. Matching what she sees with what she hears integrates her expectation with her experience.

Parent-Baby Interactions

Visual-Auditory Game

*Babies should be put on their stomachs **only** for short periods of time. They should **never** be left alone in this position. It is suitable to place your baby in the prone position when she is rested, alert, dry, and comfortable, but not just after feeding.*

- Place your baby on her belly, in the prone position.
- She will probably rest with her head to one side.
- Sit on the other side so that you are behind her.
- Say or sing her name or shake a soft-sounding rattle rhythmically.
- The sound of your voice or the rattle will capture your baby's attention.
- Wait to see if your baby lifts and turns her head toward you.
- Now sit on the other side and call her name again. This encourages her to turn to the opposite side.
- If she turns her head to one side, but not to the other side, explore this again the following week.

Making connections: matching what your baby sees with what she hears integrates her expectation with her experience.

Communication

Because you watch your baby closely, you notice by her rapt attention that she loves the sound of your voice. During these early months, your vocal repertoire quickly expands—crooning, cooing, and singing new lullabies to delight and soothe your infant. You may also hear your baby making new vowel-like sounds.

Parents often begin these face-to-face interactions with exaggerated facial expressions. They open their eyes and mouth wide to communicate surprise; they smile to show they're happy; they wrinkle their brow and frown indicating that they don't like something. Your changing facial expressions will capture your baby's interest. To keep this game going, add different sounds. Babies respond to drawn-out vowel sounds like *ahh-ohh-ooo* and vowel and consonant combinations like *woo-woo-woo* that grow in intensity. Parents might then add head and upper body movements, zoom in closer to their baby, and then move away. Notice how your baby responds when your voice gets louder or softer and when you move your face closer, then away. Delighted by these thrilling interactions, your baby may respond by smiling, or she may turn away to absorb her experience, then turn back for more. The more of your baby's responses that you notice when playing with her, the easier it will be to recognize how her movement development enhances her play interactions.

Your two-month-old baby's ability to turn her head to each side lets her regulate her excitement by turning toward or away from stimulation in social interactions.

Parent-Baby Interactions

Vocalizing Vowels

- Exaggerate your facial expressions—for instance, with a surprised look.
- For variety, try flicking your tongue quickly in and out of your mouth while moving toward and away from your baby.

Vocalizing Vowels.

- Improvise by softly vocalizing vowel sounds like *ahh, ohh, ooo,* etc.
- If your baby is still interested, or on another day, advance and retreat as you vocalize *woo-woo-woo.*

The variations suggested allow you to extend your playtime as long as your baby is actively engaged and enjoying the interaction.

Mapping Action Systems

In their investigation of the consequences of "self-produced locomotion" in *Current Directions in Psychological Science,* early infant development researchers Bennett Bertenthal, Joseph Campos, and Rosanne Kermoian report, "First and foremost our research program shows that some of the most significant early experiences are those produced by the infant's own actions." My longitudinal video studies of the baby's movement development also confirm that babies are not just passively responding to their environment, they are searching out information, all the while learning about themselves and their environment through their ongoing movement and actions. The three systems that are activated through your baby's actions are

- the vestibular system,
- the kinesthetic and proprioceptive system,
- the visceral system.

Let's look at these systems in more detail, then at a vignette that illustrates how these systems interact with each other.

Vestibular System

It is common knowledge that our sense of balance is located in the inner ear (vestibular mechanism). What isn't commonly known is that the vestibular system analyzes movements throughout our whole body, contributing to the awareness of where we are in space and linking up to all forms of sensory information. Think of all the actions your baby will learn from infancy to toddlerhood that depend on the smooth functioning of this system: visual-movement coordination, locomotion, balance and equilibrium responses that we continue to rely on as adults. These are the essential abilities that build a baby's body-confidence and self-esteem.

Kinesthetic and Proprioceptive System

When lying in the supine position on the floor, your two-month-old baby waves, circles, and cycles her arms and exercises a variety of kicking patterns, enhancing her motor development. Through these patterns of flexion and extension, she can sense how each part of her body moves, the relationships of her arms and legs to each other, and where each part is in space. Sensing the movement of her arms and legs contributes to your baby's growing kinesthetic awareness, informing her of where each part of her body is, how it is moving, and the quality of rest between activities. She receives this proprioceptive and kinesthetic information through her skeletal-muscular system (receptors in the bones, joints, ligaments, and muscles).

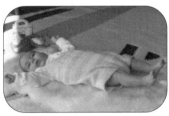

Sensing the movement of her arms and legs.

Your baby's fine sense of touch in her tactile body explorations provides her with essential information that contributes to her developing body awareness. Eye-hand coordination and tactile investigations will also inform her about the special properties of toys, objects, and her environment.

Visceral System

This system is in charge of sensing moment-to-moment visceral changes. Signals from the organs, glands, blood vessels, and nerves indicate their state of rest and activity. This internal system sends signals that make you feel hungry, calm, nervous, or joyful. Your baby is tuned in to these internal changes and, in a nonverbal way, lets you know how he is feeling: crying if he is hungry, squirming if he has indigestion, or cooing when he is satisfied. With this additional information, let's look again in more detail at the vignette describing Colm's experience.

47

Colm is lying in the prone position with his head turned to one side. He explores by bringing his hand to his mouth, extending and sliding his arm on the surface of the sofa, following his hand with his eyes. The novelty of Colm's experience—mouthing his hand, extending and flexing his arm, feeling the different textures he touches, and watching the movements he makes—provides him with a wide variety of new internal and external sensations. When he finishes exploring, he looks up and smiles to express his pleasure.

Colm experiences many pleasurable aspects in his hand-to-mouth exploration: mouthing his hand, sliding his hand over the plushy texture of the sofa (tactile sensors), moving his arm (kinesthetic sense), and watching the movement of his hand (visual processing). What begins as a hand-to-mouth action is also a complex interaction between Colm's external environment (touch and vision) and his internal environment experienced through proprioceptive and visceral systems. Antonio Damasio, in his book, *The Feeling of What Happens,* informs us that the musculoskeletal division "…can be used both to express internal states as well as to help describe the outside world." What this means in terms of our vignette is that the movement of Colm's arm provides him with internal information from his joints and muscles, and his arm action sliding over the plushy sofa provides him with information about his environment. Now we can understand how Colm's ongoing interaction with his environment activates many body systems, sending a variety of different messages simultaneously to his central nervous system.

What is important for parents to understand is that babies make vital brain connections through their body movements and sensory experiences, and in this way they develop an enriched nervous system. Candace Pert, in her book, *Molecules of Emotion,* states that it is important that we think of the brain as not only for "…merely filtering and storing this sensory input, but for associating it with other events or stimuli occurring simultaneously at any synapse or receptor along the way—that is, learning." The essential ingredient for your baby's success in learning is the feeling of pleasure he experiences in his actions and interactions. Candace Pert goes on to explain how "…emotions and bodily sensations are thus intricately intertwined, in a bidirectional [two-way communication] network in which each can alter the other. Usually this process takes place at an unconscious level, but it can also surface into consciousness under certain conditions, or be brought into consciousness by intention." How do we infer intention and pleasure in Colm's vignette? We can see Colm's intention and pleasure by the way he repeats the action and smiles.

Reflexes

Based on her extensive and dynamic work in expanding the traditional approach to reflexes in the developmental movement process, Bonnie Cohen states, "It is important to note that when we look at integrated movement, we are not seeing isolated reflexes, but rather their underlying support and influence on the movement." We discussed the oral rooting reflex in Chapter 1; this common reflex elicits a functional response in feeding and underlies head rotation. You will also have experienced the "grasp reflex" that occurs when you touch the palm of your baby's hand and she grips your finger strongly. This palmar grasp reflex underlies hand grasp and arm flexion. Newborns exhibit a number of reflexes that become integrated into more complex patterns of movement from four to six months of age. Let's now look at two more reflexes.

Moro Reflex

If a baby in the supine position hears a loud noise or if he experiences a sudden change in position that causes his head to fall back when being handled, his reaction is called the Moro reflex. During the first phase of this startle reflex, the baby's arms and hands extend. Typically, the baby also opens his mouth and he might cry. During the second phase of the reflex, the baby flexes his head and may wrap his arms across his body in an embrace or just bring his arms together to regain his composure, once he is in a comfortable position.

Mara touches the back of her head with her left hand. Her eyes look toward the felt touch.

To lessen the chances of your baby being startled:
- *Support your baby's head.*
- *Handle your baby gently but firmly before lifting.*
- *Avoid jerky movements that shake or jostle your baby.*
- *Lift and lower your baby slowly and smoothly.*

The ATNR is integrated into more purposeful actions, like swiping at toys or batting a mobile.

Asymmetrical Tonic Neck Reflex

At two months of age, a familiar reflex is the asymmetrical tonic neck reflex (ATNR), commonly referred to as the "fencing" position. When your baby turns his head to the right, he may extend his right arm and leg and flex his left arm and leg. The same holds true for the opposite side. However, head rotation does not always cause this response in every baby. The fencer reflex underlies eye-hand coordination. You will notice that this reflex is integrated into a more purposeful action when your baby, at three months of age, reaches out to bat a mobile.

Coordinated Movement

By the end of the second month, your baby is gaining control of her arms and legs. You may now notice her lying on her back, kicking and cycling her legs and waving her arms (see video clips on page 47). In the months to come, when you see your toddler walking, hopping, and jumping for joy, you can look back and see the foundation for these locomotion patterns in the simple flexion and extension patterns of your two-month-old baby.

Beginning in Prone

The following Parent-Baby Interaction is explored with your baby in the prone position. Your two-month-old baby is beginning to use her arms in prone and by placing her in this position on your body, you will feel her little hands gently push against you. When you add soft humming sounds, your baby will feel sound vibrations coming from your chest that will soothe her. Through participating in these pleasant body-to-body interactions, your baby will gradually become more comfortable on her tummy.

Parent-Baby Interactions

Baby's Body Comfort in Prone

Continue with the same exploration you were introduced to last month. Your baby may push against your body to lift her head up.

- Place your baby on her back on a clean blanket on a carpet or mat on the floor.
- Lie down on your back beside her.
- Flex your knees, raise your legs one after the other, and place your feet flat on the floor.
- Roll to your side and take your baby in your arms.
- Bring your baby to your chest and, holding her securely, roll onto your back.
- Lying on your back, support your baby to rest in the prone position on your body.

Adult Movement Explorations

Head Lifting and Turning

Whenever you lie down, yield to gravity and allow your body to be supported by the floor. Release any breath holding.

- Prepare on a carpeted floor and/or an exercise mat.
- Lie down in prone with your forehead on the mat and your arms extended overhead.
- Slide both arms toward your body; place your arms in the primitive flexed position.
- Lift and turn your head to the right and rest your head on the floor.
- Breathe easily throughout the movement.
- Keep your forearms in contact with the floor.
- Lift and turn your head to the left and rest your head on the floor.
- Notice when your head is briefly in midline as you turn to each side.

51

Explore turning your head to each side a few times.

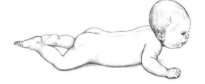

A baby can lift and turn her head to each side, but can't maintain her head in midline yet.

Notice the ease in moving or any tension you feel in your head, neck, and shoulders. Is it easier to turn your head to one side? How does the rest of your body feel?

Roll over onto your back and rest with your knees flexed and your feet flat on the floor. Continue the breathing and movement explorations introduced in Chapter 1.

In Your Journal

What are you discovering about yourself through your breathing and movement explorations? Do you observe and listen more attentively to your baby? Notice if your baby calms down when you are holding him close to you and you are humming, cooing, or singing to him – he may be enjoying the sound vibrations resonating from your chest. Does your baby prefer your voice when you speak louder or softer?

The more you use your body to sense, feel, and become aware of your own responses, the more you will learn about your baby's movement development and subtle preverbal communication cues.

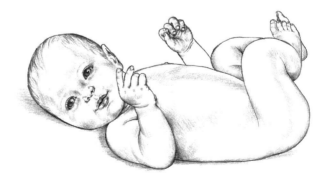

Two-Month Highlights

Body Awareness
- Hand-to-mouth
- Mouth-to-hand
- Eye-hand coordination

Movement Development and Learning
- Reflexes—grasp, Moro, ATNR
- Lifting head in prone at 45°
- Mouthing hands
- Waving and circling arms
- Kicking and cycling legs
- Tracking objects
- Attracted to brightly colored objects
- Looking for source of sound

Communication and Social Interactions
- Responds to facial expressions
- Responds and elicits smiling
- Mimics tongue wagging
- Turns toward and away from stimulation
- Enjoys body-to-body contact
- Face-to-face dialogues
- Cries
- Makes sounds

Discovery in Play with Two Hands

3

Three Months

Your three-month-old baby is more visually aware of his surroundings. You may notice that, with improved head control in the prone position, your baby begins to support himself on his forearms. He follows with curiosity and interest people who move beyond his immediate body space. Now that he is more comfortable on his tummy, you may catch him smiling at you or someone else he is watching from across the room. This shows that he is beginning to develop his orientation skills, in particular to locate people in his environment. Although prone is not a functional play position for your baby yet, when he is awake he will enjoy being in this position for brief periods of time. Just as you become used to a new movement, look, or sound from your baby, he is moving on to new frontiers of experiencing and learning. At the same time, you may notice a quizzical look or a special way of smiling that may become his signature expression, the look you will recognize as unique to him.

Perception is necessary for controlling movement just as movement is necessary for obtaining perceptual information. Perception and movement compose a cycle that is action. Action in the environment is the root of the ecological self.... We are what we do.

— David Lee,
The Perceived Self

A baby can engage in hand-to-hand play and can hold on to a rattle placed in his hand.

Mara cuddles and nuzzles with her grandmother.

Movement Becomes Symmetrical and Purposeful

Mastery of symmetrical movements and midline orientation is dominant for your three-month-old baby. For example, lying on his back, he can hold his head in midline for long periods of time with more bilateral activity. Your baby now discovers he can bring both arms symmetrically to his chest and grasp his hands together at the midline of his body. Tucking his chin, he can look down at his hands. His legs assume the familiar "frog-leg" posture as his feet contact each other at the midline.

Your three-month-old baby is quite content to develop his body awareness within the space he occupies, which is defined by the reach of his arms and legs. It is important for your baby to be on a firm, flat surface so that he can interact with the force of gravity from a physical orientation that is developmentally appropriate. He doesn't experience his own body or his world around him the same way if he is propped up in an infant seat. I have seen adults sit on a chair or sofa and watch or talk to their baby from this position. You may want to encourage other adults, who are in day-to-day contact with your baby, to be on the floor and play at your baby's level, as you are learning to do.

With improved head control and increased spinal extension developing from the head downward, the pelvis moves closer to the floor, and your baby can begin to support himself on his forearms in prone. Your baby's ability to tuck his chin when he's in prone is a significant and important development for all his visual play explorations. When you hold your baby close to you in the upright position, your baby is learning to hold his head in line with his body, without letting it fall forward, backward, or to one side.

Mara watches her grandmother's mouth and listens to her playfully make whistling and chirping sounds. Her grandmother can tell by Mara's enthralled expression that she is enjoying these musical sounds, which enhances their relationship.

Reaching and Batting a Mobile

Primitive reflexes begin to disappear as your baby gains postural control and as her actions become more purposeful. She is beginning to orient herself to objects in her surroundings, especially moving objects like mobiles. Watching the colored figures or shapes move keeps your baby interested, but now she will spend longer periods of time trying to contact the mobile, using new movement skills. Lying on her back, she can focus, direct her aim, and reach for an interesting object. Keeping her hand closed provides more control so she can contact and bat a specific target. Through these actions, your baby continues to refine her eye-hand coordination.

Over the next few months, you will notice how your baby develops her reach, grasp, and handling skills. Even now, as her hands unfurl, she can hold on to a rattle if you place it in her hand. She can pull and tug soft toys with both hands. However, her ability to voluntarily release an object will not develop until she is able to sit independently, freeing her hands to begin to develop her fine motor skills.

The three-month-old baby's head-eye-hand coordination has developed so she can actively focus, reach out, and direct her aim to contact a specific figure.

Batting a Mobile Vignette

When Mara sees the blue figure, she responds with surprise (open mouth, wide eyes, and open hands), but it is the red figure she prefers. She uses a fisted hand that provides her with more control to reach and contact a particular figure on the mobile. Mara may be attracted by its color, or it may be the friendly animated expression of the figure that fascinates her. She has made the little figure twirl and the twirling motion sustains her interest as she follows it with her eyes.

Batting a Mobile Vignette.

Body Awareness

Babies develop their body awareness through touch and movement in their body-to-body explorations. Your three-month-old can maintain his head in midline for longer periods of time and bring his hands to midline in hand-to-hand and hand-to-chest contact. Now that he can tuck his chin, he can look down and watch his hands grasp each other. He can also bring his feet together and assume a frog-leg posture. All these actions together reinforce his developing body awareness. In the following body game with your baby, you will name the parts of the body that he will explore over the next few months.

Parent-Baby Interactions

Body Naming Game

This game reinforces your baby's body awareness explorations.

- Touch one part of the body your baby is discovering, such as her hands.
- Name the body part for her. Your words can be as simple as, "(baby's name), I see you've found your hands today!"
- Next month you can add knees.
- At five months, add fingers and toes.

Diapering Game

You can expand the Body Naming Game.

- Hold both of your baby's hands up.
- Say, "Here are (baby's name) hands!"
- Hold both of your baby's feet up.
- Say, "Here are (baby's name) feet!"
- Circle your baby's belly button.
- Say, "Here is (baby's name) belly button! Round and round it goes!"
- Next month, add your baby's knees.

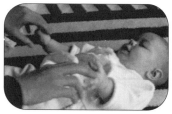

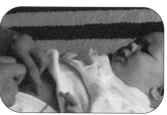

You will be reinforcing your baby's body awareness by touching and naming the parts of her body that she is exploring.

You know how much your baby enjoyed having you sing vowel sounds to him. Vocalizing face-to-face, he probably noticed that your voice got louder as your face moved in closer and as you moved away from him, the sound of your voice got softer. By the end of this month your baby will be crying less and vocalizing more, and he may surprise you with a belly laugh. Making sounds—from crying to laughing, and from vocalizing to babbling—exercises and strengthens your baby's diaphragm and, of course, expands his communication repertoire. By exploring your own vocalizing, you may discover that you can more readily distinguish the different sounds your baby makes to communicate his different needs.

Adult Sound and Movement Explorations

Vocalizing Vowels

You can expand your breathing awareness by adding a new vocal exploration: sustaining vowel sounds.

- Exhale *la-la-la-la-la.*
- Continue for a few complete cycles, becoming aware of your reflexive inhalation.
- Vocalize *eee-eee* for a full exhalation and continue with…
- *Ay-ah-oh-oo* each on a full exhalation.
- On one exhalation, vocalize a sequence one after the other: *ee-ay-ah-oh-oo.*
- Explore different pitches.
- Sing a verse to a song such as "Row, Row, Row Your Boat" on one breath.

In the beginning, you may not be able to sustain a vowel very long or sing one verse of a song or nursery rhyme on one breath. With practice, you will notice a remarkable improvement in your ability to do so over time. Notice that your abdomen doesn't protrude when you vocalize. If you aren't sure, review the breathing exploration in Chapter 1 by placing a book on your abdomen, in the supine position, and observing what happens when you vocalize.

Rolling Side to Side

When you lie down on the floor (on your back or your abdomen, right or left side), allow your body to be supported by the floor. Release any breath holding. In this exploration, you will become aware of your vertical midline.

- Breathe easily.
- Lie down on your back with knees flexed and feet flat on the floor (semi-supine position).
- Raise your legs one at a time off the floor.
- Place your hands on your knees.
- Notice the contact of your back with the floor.
- Keep your head-to-tailbone alignment as you roll toward your left side.
- Move your left arm and left leg toward the floor at your left side.
- Slowly move your right arm and leg to lie on top of your left arm and leg. Rest for a moment, then…
- Keep your head-to-tailbone alignment as you roll toward your right side.
- Move your right arm and right leg toward the floor at your right side.
- Slowly move your left arm and left leg to lie on top of your right arm and leg.
- Did you notice how one side contacts the floor, then your spine, then the other side?
- Explore rolling slowly to each side several times.

You may notice that your movements in everyday activities are freer. With new movement options, you are expanding your movement vocabulary during these floor explorations.

Any new body position you assume will be a novelty to your baby. When she is lying on the floor on her back, lie down nearby. With your hands on your knees, roll over on your side to face her and notice her response. This movement is done with intention, whereas in the next Parent-Baby Interaction, you are casually lying beside your baby observing her.

Add a folded towel under your head to keep your head-to-tailbone alignment.

61

When you are close by, your baby can take the lead in social interaction.

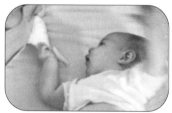

Pulling and tugging a soft toy animal.

Parent-Baby Interactions

FloorPlay

Each month you will expand your movement repertoire by exploring different positions on the floor. Your baby will be more content when you are at her level and she may actively take the lead in play because you are close by. The more comfortable you are in moving your body in and out of a variety of positions, the more spontaneous your interactions will be with your baby.

- Place your baby on her back on a clean blanket on a carpet or mat on the floor.
- Lie on your side facing your baby; she may roll to face you.
- Lie close enough to your baby that she can reach you to touch you or your face with both hands.
- Change sides to encourage your baby to roll to both sides.

Especially for you: babies often vocalize with their body movements. Your baby may make the sweetest sound as she reaches out to touch your face with both hands.

FloorPlay Variation

- Hold a soft toy or facecloth and let your baby reach out to grasp the other end with both hands.
- Provide a little resistance.
- Notice how she uses both hands together to tug and pull.
- Using both hands, she may tug hard enough to pull it out of your hands.

Note: at this age, don't leave your baby unattended on the floor or with toys.

In Your Journal

Write down what you experienced in your breathing, vocalizing, and movement explorations. Vocalizing helps to energize your breathing and increases your feeling of vitality.

Have you noticed your baby can tuck his chin and watch his hands when he is lying in the supine (on his back) position? When you are holding him, does he cuddle and nuzzle into your neck? Are you becoming more aware of how you can encourage your baby's movement responses by where you position yourself in relation to him?

This month your social baby may smile a lot at people he knows well. Jot down the first time you hear your baby laugh out loud. When you are conversing with your baby face-to-face, what new expressions and sounds are you noticing? Change the pitch of your voice when you are talking to him and notice his preferences. Each day he adds more delightful responses.

Three-Month Highlights

Body Awareness
- Hand-to-hand in supine
- Foot-to-foot

Movement Development and Learning
- Symmetry and midline orientation
- Tucking chin
- Watching own hands in supine
- Eye-hand coordination
- Reaching and batting mobiles
- Tussling toys with both hands
- Voluntary grasp
- Tracking people visually
- Tracking brightly colored objects

Communication and Social Interactions
- Cuddles and nuzzles
- Reaches with both hands to touch you
- Smiles at you across a room
- Laughs out loud
- Cries less and vocalizes more
- Face-to-face dialogues

Moving from Motivation to Mastery

4

Four Months

You will find each day a delight as you watch, listen, and learn about your baby's new explorations, which begin literally at her fingertips. As your four-month-old looks down to watch her hands, she can make scratching sounds on a textured carpet and handle a toy in new ways. She can grasp a toy nearby, but reaching out for a toy with one hand is not yet in her movement repertoire. You will learn how she prepares for this dynamic action next month. Make sure you select age-appropriate toys for your baby to play with. For your four-month-old, it may be a chain of multicolored links or rings that captures her attention. Her desire to explore motivates her to set up her own problem-solving tasks so that she learns by discovering her own solutions. When your baby grasps the toy she wants, she builds her body-confidence and self-mastery. When you think about it, curiosity, interest, problem solving, and making her own discoveries in play are the skills she will use for all her future learning. Let's look in more detail at how your baby's activities unfold this month.

Learning occurs when the nervous system repeats its exploratory activity on an object of the environment until it is successful, i.e. satisfies the intention.

— Moshe Feldenkrais,
The Elusive Obvious

A baby can maintain her head in midline, supported on forearms.

At four months, your baby's purposeful movements are expanding with an increasing ability to alternate coordinated actions. She can now maintain her head in midline in the prone position. This key development facilitates her movement explorations. By keeping her head at 90° in midline, your baby can coordinate both sides of her body, bring her hands together, and look down at her hands to participate in more purposeful play and tactile explorations.

Visual Processing

When your three-month-old baby was lying on her back, she could bring her hands to her chest, grasp them together, and look at her hands. She can perform the same action this month, but while lying on her belly.

Your four-month-old baby's ability to watch her hands while playing in the prone position indicates that her visual system is maturing. The coordination she is developing in eye-hand explorations is a result of her improved ability to maintain head control, especially tucking her chin (head flexion) to look down at her hands. Last month, your baby could horizontally track a moving object from one side to the other. This month, the range of your baby's visual field expands to include vertical and diagonal tracking. Another visual achievement this month is your baby's ability to see full-spectrum color.

Infant Seats, Baby Swings, Baby Exercisers, and Playpens

We mentioned in the last chapter that infant seats inhibit your baby's freedom to move. Overuse of infant seats, baby swings, baby exercisers, and playpens restricts the natural body movements that are essential for your baby to become an independent traveler, an active participant in play, and an explorer in the environment. The following specific information about these seats and playpens may help you make an informed decision about how much you want to use them each day.

Overuse of infant seats and baby swings

- inhibits both spinal movement and active visual exploration because the seat keeps a baby's body at a 45° angle,
- prevents a baby of 4 to 5 months from using his forearms for weight bearing and weight shifting, which are necessary for reaching,
- limits locomotor explorations and perceptual development at all levels from 6 to 12 months.

Overuse of baby exercisers and bouncers

- inhibits a baby's spinal development in prone, supine, and side-lying positions that will later be needed to support independent sitting,
- leads a baby to use his feet prematurely to support his body weight before he develops the ability to stand independently,
- holds a baby in the upright position, preventing age-appropriate movement and exploration.

Overuse of a playpen in the locomotion stage

- prevents development of spatial awareness,
- confines a baby's exploring nature and her ability to move out into her environment,
- prevents spontaneous interactions and free play,
- limits a baby's discovery of changing viewpoints of the room,
- limits opportunities to perceive toys and objects from different perspectives.

Important Notes

Infant car seats: I am not, of course, referring to car seats that are essential for your baby's safety and must be used at all times.

Walkers: studies have shown that walkers pose a potential risk when babies are left unattended in them. As well, walkers prevent development of a baby's postural control when weight bearing and weight shifting while walking.

Freedom to Move

Babies need unstructured free time to play on the floor each day. They develop body-confidence when they can move freely at their level, on the floor. Babies gather valuable information during these physical interactions with gravity. Through their movement explorations, babies develop their body awareness, body boundaries, and body image. In play, babies gain body experiences that facilitate their problem-solving skills. Body-confidence increases spontaneity in play and, in a receptive environment, babies can take the lead in social interactions.

Body Awareness

The following examples demonstrate what your baby may be exploring at this stage.

In the supine position:

- hand-to-hand, foot-to-foot, ankle-to-ankle, hands-to-knees explorations to develop body awareness and body boundaries.

In the prone position:

- support on forearms to develop hand-to-hand play, body awareness, and tactile explorations,
- support on hands to extend elbows for strength to do body push-ups,
- spinal extension and head flexion to develop muscles for rolling over,
- weight-shift explorations to each side to facilitate reaching.

You will notice that your four-month-old baby's kicking is more coordinated. She symmetrically flexes and extends both legs together, and moves on from the frog-leg posture. In the supine position, she can raise her knees

Hands on knees increase her tactile body awareness.

higher, extend her elbows, and hold on to her knees with her hands. Tucking her chin, she watches her hands in the tactile explorations that increase her awareness of her body. Notice that your baby extends her elbows when she is lying on her back, but not in the prone position. This ability will develop next month.

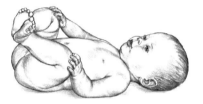

This four-month-old lifts her knees higher and reaches down with her hands to hold her knees.

Adult Movement Explorations

Hands on Knees

This exercise supports and eases any tension in your lower back. You can do it before and/or after the Adult Movement Explorations at the end of the chapter.

- Lie down on a mat or carpeted floor with knees flexed and both feet on the floor.
- Raise one leg at a time so that your feet are off the floor.
- Place your hands on your knees, and breathe easily.
- Slowly move one knee away from your chest.

- Your arm extends and maintains contact with your knee.
- Alternate knees, and notice one arm is flexing as the other arm is extending.
- Continue for three complete cycles; finish with both knees and arms flexed.
- Lower your legs one at a time.
- Extend one leg at a time and rest.

Note: raise and lower your legs one at a time to support your lower back so that your spine stays in contact with the floor.

Variation

- With hands on knees, make little circles with both knees moving in the same direction.
- Reverse the direction.
- Lower your legs one at a time.
- Extend one leg at a time and rest.

Notice the way your back contacts the floor during the movement.

Spinal Patterns

Your baby's spinal curves are shaped by body movement and supported body positions. From the primary C-curve shape of the spine, the second curve to develop is the neck curve (cervical curve). Your baby's antigravity movements—lifting, turning, extending, and flexing her head—develop the shapely neck curve. Have you noticed it in your four-month-old baby?

In prone, she can now fully extend her spine, release her arms from the floor, and extend her legs into space. In this pivot-prone position, both elbows are flexed and off the floor. She will practice until she can move smoothly between pivot-prone (with both arms off the floor) and weight bearing in prone (with both forearms on the floor). Next month, you will see her extend one arm after the other and she will look more like she's swimming. At

A baby in pivot-prone position.

70

six months, she will be able to extend both arms together and look like she's flying. The spinal patterns contribute to your baby's body image development, and help her distinguish the front of her body from the back.

Symmetrical Patterns

When your baby is in prone, she can support herself on her forearms, push up onto both hands, and begin to extend her elbows. These symmetrical push patterns are based on the developing spinal patterns that provide the body's internal core support. It is the symmetrical foundation necessary for her to develop integrated postures, binocular vision, and the ability to cross her body's midline. You will become familiar with this symmetrical pattern during the next few months as prone becomes a functional play position for your baby.

Rolling to Side Lying

Your baby rolls from her back to side lying by symmetrically flexing her hips and knees. Lying on her side is important for tactile stimulation and developing antigravity lateral flexion, as well as for eye-hand coordination during play in this position. Positioning yourself to either side of your baby facilitates this development.

Self-Motivated Play

During the fourth month, your baby is learning a great deal about her hands. She explores different textures and surfaces, all of which stimulate her tactile awareness. For example, scratching a rough carpet, grasping a soft fuzzy bear or a hard smooth rattle—each sends a different sensory message to her nervous system. Her primary grasp is called a *palmar grasp* because she uses the palms of her hands to pick up objects. Although your baby can't voluntarily release toys from her hands, she can tug and pull a toy, like a chain of links, out of her hand. The act of mouthing their toys provides babies with specific tactile information like the qualities of hard or soft.

A baby can move from the pivot-prone position to support herself on both hands.

71

Babies build body-confidence and self-esteem when they follow their curiosity, interest, and desire. Considering the many possibilities provided in her environment, what your baby chooses to play with indicates the uniqueness of her development. In self-initiated play, her motivation and problem-solving skills may propel her toward a more advanced level of exploration. As Lois Bly notes in her book, *Motor Skills Acquisition in the First Year*, these problem-solving sessions give variability to the developmental process. Her calm attention span lengthens when she initiates and completes the play sessions at her own pace, which forms the groundwork for your baby's success in self-mastery and learning. The following vignettes provide clear examples of self-directed learning.

Action, Sensation, and Amusement Vignette.

Action, Sensation, and Amusement Vignette

Mara is playing on her belly on a black and white striped carpet. Raking the carpet with her fingers, she discovers a lot about the texture of the carpet and how she can make new scratching sounds with her hands. While playing, she makes a clicking sound in her mouth and smiles, amused at her own actions.

Mara is exploring something important while she is raking and scratching a textured carpet. This activity prepares her sensitive hands for stronger actions like supporting her body on her hands. While playing, Mara smiles. What causes her to smile? Is it the sensation in her mouth, the sound she hears, the tactile sensation in her hands, or the clicking sound she makes? Mara connects her actions with her sensations, and a smile bubbles up from within. In this situation, Mara is not responding to someone smiling at her, nor is she looking up to engage someone to elicit a smile. She simply finds her sensory experience pleasurable and her spontaneous actions amusing.

Moving from Motivation to Mastery

The following vignette provides us with a new understanding of how a baby's focused attention assists her in planning and practicing her actions to get what she wants. In self-initiated play, babies do not just passively receive sensory information; they actively choose what they will focus on and direct their attention to achieve their goals. What we know about four-month-old babies and color vision is that they have refined their ability to perceive the whole spectrum of color, an ability that opens up tantalizing explorations for them. Let's see what Mara's favorite color is.

> ### Yellow Link Vignette
>
> *Mara is playing with a chain of multicolored links that are all the same shape. When we follow the path of Mara's focus, we notice that she is looking at the yellow link and she actively chooses the color she wants. Since she can grasp toys but can't yet release them, Mara tugs and pulls the chain to get one hand free, and then she diligently practices preshaping her thumb and index finger in the same shape of the link. Then, she grasps the yellow link with one hand, uses her mouth to hold the middle of the link, and without looking at her other hand, she grasps the other end of the link. Completing her play episode, she smiles and looks up with bright eyes to share her mastery.*

Action Plans

As soon as your baby can bring her hands together, she finds things to grasp, hold, and explore. It was once thought that a baby's play with toys and objects was limited at this age to simple grasping, and that babies were not able to handle toys and objects in a purposeful way. We see that Mara's desire and problem-solving abilities prompt her to go much further. With concentrated attention, Mara actively focuses on the color she wants until she devises a highly sophisticated grasping

Yellow Link Vignette.

73

technique: shaping her thumb and index finger in imitation of a link, then hooking them through the hole of the link she wants, she holds the middle of the link with her mouth and clasps the other end of the link with her other hand without looking. Mara has succeeded in adding a more advanced grasping skill to her present handling repertoire. When babies carry out their intentions from motivation to mastery, they develop self-confidence in directing their own learning agenda.

We have seen that the links Mara plays with are all the same size and shape, differing only in color. Mara is able to actively direct her focus on the yellow link. At four months, babies can now distinguish between colors that are closer together, like yellow from green, and they can also recognize similar hues within a color group.

From Desire to Dialogue

How does a four-month-old expressively communicate her mastery to an adult? Even without words, Mara's smile and bright eyes convey it all. Mara did what she intended to do. She is beaming, her expressive way of communicating and sharing her pleasurable learning experience with an attentive parent, caregiver, or other observer. Of course, she can't verbally go into detail about how she planned her actions or how she figured out how to grasp the yellow link for the first time, but that's what is so intriguing about closely observing your baby's daily explorations. The following key points summarize Mara's learning experiences:

- Motivation—she acts on her curiosity and interest.
- Self-direction—she needs no encouragement to explore and play.
- Self-mastery—she regulates her attention.
- Problem solving—she successfully completes her activities.
- Social interaction—she communicates her pleasure.

Weight Shift: Preparing to Reach

Babies shift their weight sideways to support themselves on one arm, so they can free the other hand for reaching. Your baby's developing head and trunk control in this position often leads to overreaching, and her head may lean a little toward the side to which she has shifted. She will need practice shifting her weight to each side before she can coordinate her upper body and develop enough control to reach out toward her goals and get what she wants. You will learn more about this significant development next month.

Adult Movement Explorations

If you have had abdominal surgery, check with your doctor before doing these movement explorations.

Symmetrical Yield and Push Pattern

- Lie down on the floor in the prone position.
- Place your forehead on the floor and extend your arms overhead.
- Exhale *la-la-la*.
- Simultaneously lift your head and upper torso and…
- Slide both arms toward your body, and position your elbows under your shoulders.
- Support yourself on your forearms, and maintain the height of your upper body.
- Your forearms and hands should maintain contact with the floor.
- Keep your pelvis and legs, all the way to your feet, in contact with the floor.
- Push a little through your hands to emphasize their support.
- Explore this movement for 30 seconds or within your comfort range.

A four-month-old baby shifts her weight sideways.

75

- Simultaneously, adjust your arms in the primitive flexed position with 90° angles between the forearm and upper arm and…
- Lower your head and upper body to the floor.
- Repeat again, and raise your head and upper body as you exhale *la-la-la*.
- Position your elbows under your shoulders. Your head should be aligned with your spine in midline.
- Direct your focus forward; your eyes should not be looking up at the ceiling or down at the floor.

Explore 3 times.

Tune in to the sensation of moving your elbows and feel the movement of your scapulas (shoulder blades). Experiment with the alignment of your elbows: position your elbows under or a little forward of your shoulders.

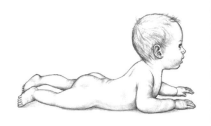

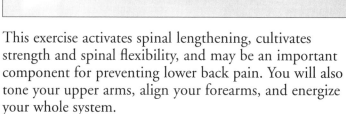

This exercise activates spinal lengthening, cultivates strength and spinal flexibility, and may be an important component for preventing lower back pain. You will also tone your upper arms, align your forearms, and energize your whole system.

Inner Organic Support

You have already learned a lot about how your breathing integrates with your body movement. In the following exploration, you will also experience how the organs provide the energetic visceral support to your skeletal-muscular system. When you are holding and feeding your baby, you can observe the soft organic undulations in her body while she is sucking, swallowing, and digesting.

Explore this exercise on a carpeted surface or a mat with a clean cover. Before you lie down, sip a little cool water, swallow, and sense the movement down your digestive tract (smaller sips make you more aware). Your digestive tract is a continuous tube, beginning with your mouth, that provides a buoyant support for your spine.

- Lie down on the floor on your back or side.
- Exhale *la-la-la* and observe the movement of your spine.
- Bring your attention to your entire digestive tract.
- You can also visualize your digestive tract as a soft flexible tube in front of your spine.
- Roll over to the prone position, supported on your forearms and…
- Repeat the symmetrical push pattern with attention to your digestive tract as a support for your spine.

Swimming 1 Pivot-Prone

Lie down on a clean padded surface.

- In the prone position, place your forehead on the floor.
- Place your arms in the primitive flexed position, with 90° angles between the forearm and upper arm.
- Exhale *la-la-la* as you simultaneously raise your upper torso and arms off the floor.
- The primitive flexed position of your arms draws your scapulas toward your spine.
- Keep your abdomen and legs in contact with the floor, all the way to your toes.
- Hold this position briefly.
- Exhale as you lower your body to the beginning position.
- Repeat and bring attention to your inner support.

- You can alternate this pattern with the symmetrical yield and push pattern.

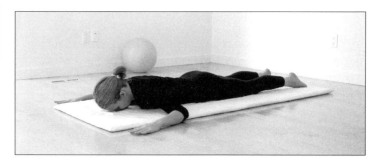

Sometime during this month, your baby smoothly alternates between the pivot-prone extension position and the symmetrical push pattern (forearm weight bearing).

Weight Shift Sideways

Sense how shifting your weight sideways prepares your baby to free the unweighted arm for unilateral reaching next month.

- Support yourself on your forearms.
- Shift your weight sideways onto your right arm.
- Return to align your head with your spine in midline.
- Shift your weight sideways onto your left arm.
- Return to align your head with your spine in midline.

Notice if your head leans to either side. If so, adjust yourself so that your head is in the upright position and centered in the midline of your body, aligning your spine head-to-tail.

78

Directing Discovery

Five Months

Your baby's fifth month marks the approaching end of the pre-locomotion stage. Soon your baby will be on the move. Five months is an ideal age to join a parent-baby group. Five-month-old babies can get used to one another by looking and watching each other at a distance, before they enter the dynamic locomotion stage. Remember: each baby is unique and even a few weeks' difference in age means a lot at this stage. In one of my parent-baby groups, a mother whose baby was three weeks younger than the others expressed concern that he seemed to be content just to watch the other babies. However, within a few sessions, he was surprising her with new movements and little squeals that looked and sounded just like those of the other babies.

Your five-month-old builds on the essential movement components she developed at four months. These integrated movements are based on symmetrical movement, midline orientation, and coordinating both hands to carry out her visual-manual explorations. Five-month-old babies explore new movements in a variety of positions, with some key developments beginning this

Development does not occur in a linear progression but as overlapping waves with each pattern being integrated and modified by the emergence of new patterns. Eventually all patterns are contained in each of the others...

— Bonnie Bainbridge Cohen,
Sensing, Feeling, and Action

month. You might see one baby lying on his back pushing with both feet to raise his pelvis off the ground (this is called bridging), while another baby may be practicing her reaching skills in the prone position, and perhaps your baby is rolling to side lying to play with a toy. The ability to stay on her side encourages your baby's development of rolling from her back to her front. Some babies will perform this action by the end of this month; however, mastery of rolling is more commonly seen in the six-month-old.

Body Awareness

With more control when she is in supine, your baby can extend her elbows and knees and hold on to her feet without rolling over or falling onto her side. She can reach, grasp, and bring her feet to her mouth, continuing her tactile explorations and expanding her body awareness. An important development is her ability to reach across her midline to use both hands to play with one of her feet.

A baby reaches across her midline to play with one foot.

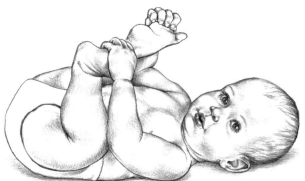

The five-month-old baby can bring hands to feet and feet to mouth.

82

Spinal Movement

The spinal movement patterns establish the baby's head-to-tail connection—in prone, supine, or side lying. What is significant during this month is that your baby rolls over to maintain a new side-lying position for play. From side lying, important movements develop: he can flex his body sideways (spinal lateral flexion) and he can rotate his body (spinal rotation). This means your baby now has a full range of control of his head. At four months, he is able to extend and flex his head in prone and begin to lift and flex it in supine (that is, he can lift his head to watch a body game), and now, while side lying, he can laterally lift and flex his head sideways.

New Movement Patterns

Spinal movements provide the internal core support necessary for your baby to begin to coordinate his arms and legs in relationship to each other and in relationship to his whole body. Two new movement patterns emerge that contribute to the development of your baby's body image. They are the symmetrical and lateral push patterns.

Symmetrical push patterns are initiated by both hands and/or both feet. These patterns help your baby differentiate his upper body from his lower body. The four-month-old supports himself on his forearms in prone. The five-month-old pushes with both hands and extends his elbows. At six months, he adds a new locomotion pattern—the symmetrical push pattern from both hands and discovers that his body slides backward!

Lateral push patterns are initiated by the hand and/or foot on one side of the body, which helps your baby define and identify each side, one from the other. She begins the movement sequence by pushing with one foot, elongating that side of her body, then reaches with her hand on the same side. Later, at seven months, your baby will use this movement pattern for belly crawling by alternating sides.

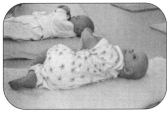

In side lying, babies can flex their bodies sideways (spinal lateral flexion) and rotate their bodies (spinal rotation).

Symmetrical push initiated from the hands.

Pushing, Reaching, and Swimming

In prone, your four-month-old could visually explore, handle, and choose a specific colored toy for mouthing, thereby prompting new responses in problem solving. Since the five-month-old has more control over shifting his weight, prone becomes an even more functional play position. In this position, he can push up onto his hands to extend his arms, he can support himself on his forearms, and he can shift his weight to either side to free one arm for reaching forward. As he practices these patterns, he may also release both arms from the floor, to swim on his belly. Indeed, at this stage, babies sometimes resemble seal pups: as one arm is flexing the other arm is extending, producing a rocking motion on the belly, and it looks like they're swimming. Practicing this swimming activity on their bellies is essential for babies to develop muscles for rolling over, standing up, and walking.

Adult Movement Explorations

Swimming 2 Pivot-Prone

- Breathe easily throughout the movement.
- Lie down on the floor in the prone position.
- Place your forehead on the floor and your arms in the primitive flexed position.
- Slide your forearms and hands toward one another, so that your middle fingers touch, creating a diamond shape.
- Exhale *la-la-la* and raise your head and upper torso off the ground.
- Lift your right arm off the floor, reach out with your hand, and extend your elbow.
- As you begin flexing your right arm, reach out with your left hand.
- From your midline outward, one arm is extending while the other arm is flexing.
- Follow with your eyes the hand that is reaching out.

84

- Notice a rocking motion on your abdomen, as you swim using a flowing movement of your arms.
- With your head in midline, lower your body to the beginning position.
- Explore within your comfort range, and without any pressure in your lower back.
- Lie on your back to rest with your knees up and your feet flat on the floor.

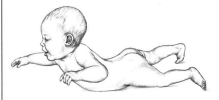

Pivot-prone develops muscles for rolling over, standing up, and walking.

Pushing from the right foot, Gabrielle elongates the right side of her body to grasp the toy.

Lateral Reaching

In prone, your five-month-old practices a variety of weight shift patterns, first initiated in the upper limbs and progressing down to the lower limbs. With more control of the sideways weight shift, your baby can now support herself by weight bearing on one arm, freeing the other arm for reaching.

In this little episode, Gabrielle illustrates this streamlined sequence. Gabrielle focuses on the toy she wants to grasp. Weight bearing on one side of her body frees the other side for greater articulation and movement. She tucks her toes and pushes off with her right foot. Elongating the right side of her body, she extends her right leg and then her right arm to reach forward. Gabrielle successfully grasps the toy with her right hand, using the same palmar grasp she did at four months. Lateral reaching is one-half of the belly-crawling pattern we will see in the locomotion stage.

Side Lying

At five months, babies still keep their arms and legs together when they roll from their backs to their sides, as they did at four months. Once babies are lying on one side, symmetry gives way to asymmetry. Your baby will begin to move her arms and her legs independently, differentiating her arms from each other, and also differentiating her legs from each other. Now she has more options for new coordinated movements between her arms and legs.

When she is lying on her side with her head on the floor, the development of lateral head righting (lifting her head up off the ground) stimulates spinal lateral flexion. These righting reactions underlie rolling of the body. The movements that your baby explores throughout this month will be the ones that she masters next month when she rolls from her back to her stomach. Rolling will be one of your baby's first locomotion patterns, allowing her to change her place in space. The experience your baby receives in rolling and playing while lying on her side is vital because it activates many body systems that

- provide the necessary tactile input to shape the ribcage,
- activate your baby's visual system, offering new perspectives of her surroundings,
- stimulate the vestibular system (sensory receptors in the inner ear),
- activate the proprioceptive and kinesthetic senses (from bones, joints, ligaments, and muscles) telling her where each part of her body is in relationship to each other, where each part is in space, and about the quality of her rest and activity.

If you think about it, how wondrous it is that the simple act of rolling and side lying can provide so many important developmental benefits.

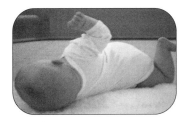

Rolling over to prone.

Play in Side Lying

Side lying is a more dynamic position for play during the fifth month. Notice that when she's lying on her side, your baby now separates her legs from each other and positions one leg in front for stability. In this position, your baby will still rest her head on a supporting surface when playing with a toy. She can extend her arm, wave a lightweight toy overhead, and visually track the movements of the toy. While lying in this position, if your baby is attracted by a sound behind her, she may respond by lifting up her head (lateral head righting) and twisting her body to look behind her (spinal rotation). If your baby suddenly rolls over from side lying onto her back, she may seem surprised because this movement is not yet within her voluntary repertoire.

You will also be experimenting with a side-lying exploration this month. You can simply lie comfortably on your side with your baby and, by doing this, encourage her to play in the side-lying position.

Play in side lying.

87

Social Interaction

Current research reveals that individuals are biologically designed to both generate and respond to rhythmic messages. What we are seeing and hearing in the following vignette is the important process of attunement: the mother's ability to adjust her response to the *feeling* underlying her baby's expressive rhythms, thereby supporting her baby's responses. Psychiatrist Daniel Stern introduced the term *vitality affects* in his book, *The Interpersonal World of the Infant,* to identify "those dynamic, kinetic qualities of feeling that... correspond to the momentary changes in feeling states involved in the organic process of being alive." The following delightful play vignette between a mother and her five-month-old baby is a good example of showing how in tune they are with each other.

Keeping the Beat Vignette.

> **Keeping the Beat Vignette**
>
> *Gabrielle's mother is at her baby's level on the floor. Gabrielle, who is playing with a soft, lightweight toy giraffe, uses a rhythmic hand gesture to bang the floor to the count of two beats. Her mother picks up the cue and vocalizes in response, "Yea-ah," matching her rhythm. As she continues to watch Gabrielle play and stay engaged, this time her mother initiates the interaction. She zooms in closer to Gabrielle and, at the same time in a singsong voice says, "Whoop-ee!" Gabrielle picks up the cue and she bangs the floor again to two beats, matching her mother's rhythm.*

In this vignette, Gabrielle and her mother are not mirroring each other by using the same gesture or vocal expression, but rather they are recasting their responses to each other into a different expressive form. Stern emphasizes that, "Attunements can be made with the inner quality of feeling of how an infant reaches for a toy, holds a block, kicks a foot, or listens to a sound. Tracking and attuning with vitality affects permit one human being to 'be with' another in the sense of sharing likely inner experiences on an almost continuous basis. This is exactly our experience of feeling-connectedness, of being in attunement with another." By responding to the inner quality of Gabrielle's preverbal rhythmic responses, Gabrielle's mother is reinforcing her infant's own pleasure in her self-directed play exploration as well as their shared connection in social interaction.

Adult Movement Explorations

Spinal Reach and Pull Patterns

Efficient changes of level are initiated by the spinal reach of the head and tail and require the push patterns for support. In supine, this is readily apparent in the baby's bridging or adult's pelvic lift explorations, where the movement is initiated by a spinal reach of the tail and is supported by the symmetrical push of both feet that provides a connection between the pelvis and feet. The reach and pull patterns develop elongation and lightness in the body in relationship to space.

Pelvic Lift

- Lie down on your back and sense the alignment of your spine, head-to-tailbone.
- Add a small folded towel to keep your neck and shoulders relaxed.
- With your legs parallel, flex your knees and place your feet in full contact with the floor.
- Adjust the distance between your knees and between your feet so that they are equal.
- Keep your arms at your sides with your palms contacting the floor.
- Exhale *la-la-la*.
- Notice how your lumbar curve flattens and your tailbone reaches and curves to move upward.
- Slowly lift your spine off the floor, one vertebra at a time. Notice if your hip joints extend symmetrically.

- Support yourself by actively pressing your feet into the floor. You will be resting on top of your shoulder blades.
- Maintain this position for several breaths.
- Exhale *la-la-la,* as you lower your body, vertebra by vertebra to the floor.
- Extend one leg after the other and rest in between.
- Explore 3 times.
- This movement should not cause any pain and is not appropriate for individuals with back pain or joint problems.
- Every so often during each month, review your breathing and sound explorations as outlined in Chapters 1, 2, and 3.

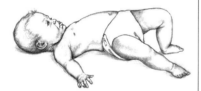

This movement may have an expressive component, like resisting getting dressed.

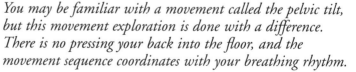

You may be familiar with a movement called the pelvic tilt, but this movement exploration is done with a difference. There is no pressing your back into the floor, and the movement sequence coordinates with your breathing rhythm.

Head Lift

- Lie down on your back. Sense the alignment of your spine, head-to-tailbone.
- Place legs parallel, flex your knees, and position your feet in full contact with the floor.
- Place your hands behind your head without interlacing your fingers and with elbows lifted.
- Nod your head up and down and sense the movement of your head.
- Uncurl and extend your arms, pointing your fingers toward your knees.
- Exhale *la-la-la* as you roll your head, neck, and upper torso off the floor.

The five- to six-month-old baby reaches and lifts her head up, with chin tucked, in response to an auditory, visual, or touch stimulation.

- Look at your fingertips and notice how you tuck your chin (head flexion) to look at your hands.
- Become aware of your reflexive inhalation.
- Exhale *la-la-la,* lowering to the floor, vertebra by vertebra.

- Simultaneously flex your elbows and place your hands behind your head again.
- Explore 3 times.

Option:
- You can leave your arms extended and you will notice your fingers point to the ceiling when you complete the movement.
- Lower your arms and place your hands behind your head to begin the movement again.

Note: if you have a tendency to pull your head up with your hands, place your fingertips gently behind your ears. Be attentive and move with your breathing.

Side Lying: Spinal Lateral Flexion
- Lie down on your right side.
- Extend your right arm and place the palm of your hand on the floor.
- Rest your head on your right arm.
- Place your left hand at chest level, elbow flexed and lifted.
- Keep both legs and feet together and maintain your balance or…
- Actively position your left foot in front for control and stability.
- Maintain your spinal alignment, head-to-tail.
- Simultaneously exhale *la-la-la* and raise your head and torso upward as your right hand slides along the floor.
- Notice that lateral flexion of the spine occurs.
- Push through both hands to extend your elbows.
- Hold this position and breathe easily, keeping hands active to your fingertips.
- On your exhalation, slide your hand on the floor as you lower your torso and head to the floor.
- Rest your head on your right arm.
- Explore 3 times on one side.

Add to your awareness:

- Roll onto your back and compare both sides: is there more contact on one side? Does one half of your body seem longer than the other half of your body? Is it the elongated side?

- Slowly roll your head to each side: is your neck freer on one side? Which side?

- Roll to the other side: if you have difficulty maintaining your balance while lying on your side, place your upper foot in front of your other foot for control and stability. Your upper hip remains directly over the other hip.

Return to Yielding as a Newborn

As we transition from the pre-locomotion stage to the locomotion stage, this is a great place for you to appreciate the full extent of your baby's movement development in the prone position. Through her challenging experiences from the full-body flexion pattern of the newborn to the full-body extension pattern of the six-month-old, your baby has learned to modulate the tone of the front and back of her body in relation to gravity.

In your own movement explorations you have been developing a subtle awareness of your breathing and the soft internal support of your digestive tract. You can now bring this mindfulness to the following spinal movements. In general, although you may be tempted to close your eyes, the developmental movements are best done with eyes open, so that you are both attentive to yourself and your surroundings.

Adult Movement Explorations

Spinal Yield and Push Patterns

In a baby's development, the spinal yield and push from the head precedes the spinal yield and push from the tail. For an adult doing this exploration, it is easier to establish your body posture from a hands-and-knees position in order to sit back on your heels and begin with the spinal yield and push from the tail. Read through the following movement patterns, study the photographs, and move within a comfortable range.

From the Tail

You should be on a padded surface or carpeted floor. If you are unable to place your forehead on the floor, use a folded towel. Breathe easily.

- Begin on your hands and knees, with your elbows under your shoulders and your knees directly under your hips.

- Keep your hands active as you sit back on your lower legs, with your tailbone over your heels.

- Place your forearms and forehead on the floor and keep them there throughout the movement.

- Widen and open across your back between your shoulder blades.

- Initiate a gentle push forward from your tail, moving sequentially, vertebra by vertebra, all the way up your spine; your head rolls forward so that you roll onto the top of your head (your pelvis is in the air above your knees).

- Keep your lower legs (ankles and feet) in contact with the floor.

- Don't put all your weight on the top of your head, but gently yield into the floor.

- Breathe easily and continue the next movement, from head to tail.

Initiated from the tail.

95

Initiated from the head.

From the Head

- Begin rolling from the top of your head onto your forehead (chin moves away from your chest).
- Continue as the movement sequences back through your spine, vertebra by vertebra, and return to sitting on your lower legs with your tailbone over your heels.
- Explore this movement 3 times only.

This movement should not cause any pain. It enhances breathing and awareness of spinal movement. Don't get up quickly from this position.

Pre-Locomotion Summary

Now that you have reached the end of the pre-locomotion stage, you have gained a deeper understanding of how important your baby's movement explorations with gravity are. You have also learned that keeping your baby in an infant seat or baby exerciser for unnecessarily long periods of time would inhibit her movement and perceptual development. Missing out on this crucial experiential learning would limit your baby's body awareness explorations, her problem-solving skill development, and her ability to initiate social interactions. In other words, this would inhibit her from becoming the competent, confident, and social baby that she naturally is.

You have participated in your baby's first half-year by providing a unique learning environment for your baby, communicating in the language he knows best through body movement, expressive body language, and vocalizing. You have not just read about how babies are developing; your knowledge is based on your own embodied experience. This physical foundation provides you with a new understanding and respect for your baby's natural movement intelligence as it unfolds with your active involvement. As you and your baby literally move into the dynamic locomotion stage, your baby is well-prepared for all the new adventures just ahead.

In Your Journal

Do you notice that you are increasing the length of breath on your exhalation? Are you more aware of your reflexive inhalation? Are you able to sustain sound with more ease when you are vocalizing your vowels or singing songs to your baby?

Do you notice that your body movement is smoother and easier when you coordinate your breathing with your movement? Are you more aware of the head-tail (spinal) connection in your different body positions? Do you change body positions on the floor with greater ease?

Do you sense that you have a more dynamic body alignment when holding and carrying your baby? Write down how your breathing and movement explorations have helped you to better bond, interact, and learn about your baby's development.

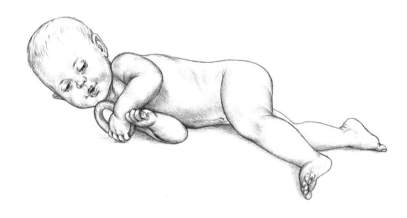

Five-Month Highlights

Body Awareness
- Hands-to-feet
- Two-hands-on-one-foot
- Feet-to-mouth

Movement Development and Learning
- Spinal Patterns
  - Flexion
  - Full extension
  - Lateral flexion
  - Rotation

- Symmetrical Patterns
  - Support on forearms
  - Support on hands

- Lateral Patterns
  - Unilateral reaching

- Bridging (pelvic lift)
- Head control in all positions
- Functional play in prone
- Rolling to side lying
- Handling Explorations
  - Playing with toys in side lying

Communication and Social Interactions
- Reaches to touch your face
- Vocalizes pleasure and frustration
- Attunement: vocal/gesture rhythms
- Watches other babies

Locomotion Stage

Six To Twelve Months

During the second half of his first year, your baby will put everything he knows into action. Babies are no longer content to move within their personal space, as in the pre-locomotion stage. The locomotion stage is defined by your baby's ability to move his body so that he can change his place in space. At the same time, your baby's communication skills expand as he adds new gestures and postures to his nonverbal repertoire. These babies are increasing their sense of timing in both actions and social interactions. Problem solving in play provides babies with an experiential base for understanding a variety of physical concepts on which they will continue to build more complex concepts.

Six-month-old baby.

Movement Development, Learning, and the Environment

Your active six-month-old explorer will soon be moving independently, going where he wants and getting what he wants. Now he can make dynamic discoveries about himself as he learns to physically interact in his environment in thrilling new ways. Mastery of rolling this month is one of the first ways babies change their place in space. In tummy play, your baby may look perplexed when he ends up pushing himself backward, moving farther and farther away from his goal. Before long, he propels himself forward across the room or yard, to reach that enticing toy. Then he will learn that the quickest way to get somewhere is creeping on his hands and knees. When babies creep in a cross-lateral pattern, they cross their midline, thereby activating both sides of the brain.

Twelve-month-old.

99

Parent-baby group.

Up to now you have been discovering the amazing developmental changes that your baby has been going through right from birth. By simply directing your attention to the more subtle movement components that make up the larger developmental milestones, such as independent sitting, standing, and walking, you will continue to have greater opportunities everyday to participate in your baby's exciting journey through the next locomotion stage.

So much is happening in her developmental dance, that you won't want to miss the changes she is actively making as she choreographs her day! As you continue to expand your developmental movement repertoire that she is experiencing for the first time (and maybe you are too!), you will enrich your interactive relationship with her by communicating through her own preverbal language of expressive movement.

A baby's budding ability to refine his movement occurs gradually over the first year. The shifting interplay between his perception and each developing movement sequence alters his orientation to gravity and space, helping him form his body image. Now, with his new mobility, your baby expands the scope of his explorations, interactions, and problem-solving abilities in his environment in different ways. The best way to enhance your baby's development is to focus on what your baby is doing each day and participate with him on the floor, delighting in his daily movement activities. These are the formative experiences that contribute to shaping your baby's world.

If you participate in a parent-baby group, keep in mind that each baby is unique and develops in tune with her own timing and rhythm. During the next few months, the differences between babies become even more apparent in both their movement and their problem-solving abilities. Their capacity for self-motivated learning and their ability to set up their own action plans, games, and goals are unique. Confident in your own baby's abilities, you can embark on this new stage, anticipating many fun-filled hours with your baby as you move, play, and learn together.

Cross-lateral creeping.

Nonverbal Communication: Postures and Gestures

After your baby achieves independence in sitting up, her arms and hands will be free for playing with toys and objects, for reaching and pulling up to a standing position, and for gestures in communication. Notice how your baby's body language increases after she reaches independent sitting. This achievement opens up a whole new world of experiences. Your baby will soon be using her hands to bang two blocks together. Making an impact like this on her environment will be a thrilling experience for her; by the time she is nine months old, she will express her delight by clapping her hands together.

In social interaction, your baby's postures and gestures literally move beyond his fingertips as he builds a rich expressive vocabulary. In the pre-locomotion stage, your baby picked up nonverbal messages in close body-to-body contact with you, his grandparents, and other adults in his immediate surroundings. In the locomotion stage, a baby will learn to interpret the nonverbal messages around him and skillfully maneuver through the complex world of adult behavior. From the other side of the room, your baby will come to recognize your expressive body language and the subtle nuances of your mood, and he will listen for your tone of voice. Babies do form impressions of people and quickly size up situations, deciding whether to interact or to redirect their attention to play elsewhere.

The roots of our adult nonverbal expressions sprout from these subtle expressive beginnings. Our body language supports and amplifies our words. Gestures lend vitality to our verbal message. However, gestures don't occur in isolation, one after the other; rather, gestures cluster together, emerging simultaneously in conversation as a natural outgrowth of our body posture. Our posture expresses our attitude or mood in relation to our current situation.

Sitting independently, she now is ready to clap her hands.

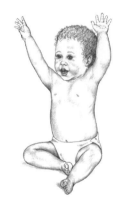

Sitting postures free arms and hands for expressive communication.

101

Rotating his forearm enables him to release toys.

The head-to-tail organization of the spine is aligned with the body's vertical axis.

The spine in a horizontal relationship to the ground.

Physical Concepts: Balance, Time, and Space

Toward the end of her first year, your baby links actions, movement patterns, and babbling into longer sequences. She integrates stability with mobility to move into and out of a variety of sitting positions. Exploring the many opportunities provided by the environment, your baby makes new connections and discoveries that form the bodily foundation of many future concepts—*in* and *out*, *up* and *down*, *here* and *there*, to name a few.

Your baby's curiosity and new movement patterns create opportunities for her to move farther afield to expand her spatial explorations. In her drive to move upward, your baby learns to change body levels and, from this new vantage point, experiences her surroundings in a different way. As your baby changes her body's position, the central head-to-tail organization of the spine is aligned with the body's vertical axis. In all movement, regardless of her body position in space, there is always this dynamic head-to-tail organization. This will become clearer when we study the eleven-month-old baby's diversity of movements through space.

In tune with herself, she will continue to develop her spatial awareness, add new locomotion skills, and seek novel experiences that challenge her balance and equilibrium. These thrilling activities provide the groundwork for your baby to be body-confident in her physical abilities, self-confident in her social relationships, and self-motivated in learning.

The selected video vignettes throughout this book illustrate the same type of experiences that unfold during your baby's FloorPlay sessions at home or in a parent-baby group. You have already learned through your baby's everyday interactions with her environment that she develops her self-mastery by seeking out her own experiments and making her own discoveries. In this next locomotion stage, along with the parent-baby interactions and baby vignettes, there are several peer-play episodes that will tickle you, touch your heart, and stimulate you to think about some of the deeper meanings that will be revealed during your baby's incredible first year.

With this overview in mind, let's learn more about your baby's locomotion process, functional actions, and expressive communication skills, month by month.

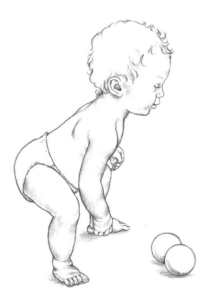

103

Dance of Development

Six Months

There is a great sense of anticipation this month now that your six-month-old baby is on the move. He discovers that his mastery in rolling from his back to his belly lets him change his body position and place in space so that now he is more active in prone and supine. On his belly, you will see him extend his whole body, appearing to "fly like an airplane." Lying on his back, he still watches his hands-to-feet play closely, and he especially enjoys the tactile stimulation of mouthing his toes. Your baby's ability to reach across his body with both hands to play with one foot continues to develop his awareness of his body's midline. With more ease, he can flex and lift his head up to watch you name the parts of his body he is exploring. This increased balance of antigravity extensor and flexor control, in prone and supine, lets your baby develop new patterns of locomotion, adding more differentiated movements of his arms and legs.

With greater control of his arms and legs, he will soon be able to coordinate his body to navigate new pathways through his environment. But for now, pushing his body across a smooth floor on his belly is an exhilarating

Between 6 and 8 months, the remaining frontal cortex begins to show a maturational rise in glucose metabolism that ... coincides with the emergence of higher cortical and cognitive abilities. For example, the infant now shows more sophisticated interaction with his surroundings.

— Harry Chugani,
  Metabolic Imaging:
  A Window on Brain
  Development and Plasticity

experience, and he lets out a holler to let everyone know what fun it is! Momentarily he forgets, or doesn't seem to care, that he is actually moving backward, farther and farther away from the toy he wants to reach. This is a period of dynamic discovery of himself—in action and interaction. Each new body coordination and pattern of mobility shapes your baby's perception. His tactile explorations in mouthing toys and practicing his handling skills are activities that teach your baby about taste, texture, and the shape of objects. A new sense of self is developing as delightful opportunities arise in his environment, inviting your baby to explore, investigate, and problem solve.

Spinal Patterns: Fly Like an Airplane

In prone, your four-month-old baby was able to extend her spine while holding her arms in the primitive flexed position. At five months, she could extend her arms, one after the other, and look as if she was swimming, in a rocking motion on her belly. At six months, she can "fly like an airplane," extending her whole body, with both arms and legs reaching into space. This pivot-prone extension pattern is the opposite of the whole body flexion pattern of the newborn. Your baby continues to practice fully extending her spine to develop the muscles she needs for rolling over, standing up, and walking.

Adult Movement Explorations

Notice your experience by focusing your attention on your breathing and your digestive tract, the soft internal support for your spine (See Chapter 4, Inner Organic Support).

Flying Pivot-Prone

- Prepare a clean padded surface such as an exercise mat or carpeted floor.
- Lie down on the floor in prone, place your forehead on the mat.
- Extend your arms overhead.
- Allow a little space between your legs, creating an X-shape with arms and legs.
- Focus your attention on your digestive tract, feeling how its soft presence in front of your spine can support your back.
- Exhale *la-la-la* and fully extend your spine (head-to-tail).
- Simultaneously lift and extend your arms and legs— try to do this *without* gripping your buttock muscles.
- Hold this position briefly.
- Maintain your inner body support as you slowly lower yourself back to the floor.
- Explore this movement 3 times.
- To rest, roll onto your back, flex your knees, and place your feet flat on the floor.

Remember that you don't need to teach your baby how to move her body, but by exploring these functional movements, you will enhance your movement awareness and your appreciation of your baby's development.

Spinal Patterns: Rolling

Mastery of rolling over from lying on his back to lying on his front is one of the first locomotion patterns that allows a six-month-old to change his place in space. His mastery of rolling from supine to prone has been evolving during the last three months. Remember your baby's progression from primitive log rolling to side lying at three months. Then at four and five months, your baby initiated rolling to the side with flexion. Around five months, your baby added lateral head righting as a transition phase, and now at six months he can complete the action with extension in prone.

If the floor space is clear, some babies will roll over from supine to prone and continue from prone to supine. With control, they are able to pause at various points in the rolling sequence between supine, side lying, and prone, or they can roll consecutively. They may begin rolling to the right side over and over, pause to look at someone or something that has captured their attention, then change direction and roll back again to the left side, covering the same territory. Earlier, you learned that it was important for babies to lift and turn their head to each side. At six months, it is important that your baby is able to roll to both sides. However, not all babies cover a lot of territory when they roll over. Your baby's purpose in rolling over may simply be to arrive in the prone position ready to play.

As Bonnie Cohen writes, "Body *rotation, rolling* and *turning* lie on a continuum from simple to more complex behavior. The reflexes underlie rotation of the head, the righting reactions underlie rolling of the body, and the equilibrium responses underlie turning of the body in space" *(Sensing, Feeling, and Action)*.

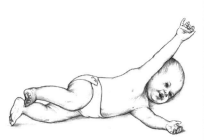

Spinal patterns differentiate the front of the body from the back of the body.

Adult Movement Explorations

Rolling over from our back to our stomach is a complex skill we learn as babies and, as adults, it still forms part of our repertoire of movements. Rolling over requires full body coordination in relation to gravity. Rolling smoothly requires a combination of accurate effort and rhythmic timing to coordinate our movement through space.

Rolling: Back to Front

- Lie down on your back with both legs extended and both arms in the primitive flexed position.
- Turn your head to face the right side.
- Reach across your chest with your left hand.
- Continue reaching and watching your hand (this will encourage head flexion).
- Make the transition through to side lying by lifting your head off the floor (lateral head righting).

- Flex your left leg as it crosses over and brushes your right leg.
- With your left knee and left hand, contact the floor.
- Notice that your right side is extended and your left side is flexed.
- Continue rolling over to prone.
- Simultaneously rotate and flex your right arm and extend your left leg, arriving in prone.

- Support yourself on your forearms with your elbows under your shoulders.
- Align your head in midline, maintaining your head-to-tailbone connection.

How would you begin the function of rolling from prone to supine? Are you able to roll in a smooth motion? When you have mastered this movement, try rolling over to one side consecutively in two or three full rotations. If you begin to feel dizzy, simply roll back slowly to where you began and breathe easily. Rolling is one of those fundamental movements from infancy that we repeat again and again.

109

FloorPlay at your baby's level.

FloorPlay

In my parenting programs I've found that many babies aren't comfortable on their bellies playing on the floor. Because they have had little experience with gravity, these babies have not integrated the earlier core spinal patterns or developed the symmetrical patterns essential to support themselves on their forearms, shift their weight side to side, and push up onto their hands to extend their elbows. These babies lack upper body strength and sufficient experience in prone to be able to shift their weight side to side and reach out for what they want. Many parents, unaware of the important role that gravity plays in their baby's development, may have used an infant seat or a baby exerciser for extended periods of time, or they may have chosen to carry their baby during most of the early months. But all babies need to gain experience interacting with the formative force of gravity.

Fortunately, even an inexperienced six-month-old baby can change rapidly. In one case, a family had been traveling for several months and carried their baby most of the time, even though she was beginning the locomotion stage. On their return, they joined my parenting group. At the first session, this timid baby watched her friend who had more movement experience pushing his body across the floor. Her parents placed her on the warm, smooth floor and got down on the floor with her. Soon, she was supporting herself on her forearms. Within several sessions this curious baby could lift her body up, look around, extend her elbows, and push herself across the floor.

At one of my developmental movement workshops for parents, a mother brought her six-month-old baby with her. She was amazed at how content her baby was on the floor! But it was evident that this baby enjoyed herself because all the parents were also on the floor exploring the same movements. Too often parents put their babies on the floor, then walk away. Later, when they see that their babies have become fussy, they wrongly conclude it's because their babies don't like playing on their tummies on the floor. Your opportunities to bond with your baby are enhanced when you get down on the floor at her level. Especially during the baby's locomotion stage, it is essential that parents set up a responsive environment and enjoy their FloorPlay together. When you are attentive to your baby's explorations and watch what she is doing, you will be amazed at how much she is learning. When she looks up, her sparkling bright eyes and little smile say it all. She is sharing her moments of self-mastery with you.

Symmetrical Push Patterns

Babies develop muscle tone and strength when they use both hands to push their whole body against the resistance of gravity. This pattern can be seen this month in a baby's push-ups and in locomotion. Both hands and/or both feet move simultaneously. In locomotion, babies push with both hands and discover that they are moving backward.

Symmetrical push patterns differentiate the upper body from the lower body.

Your baby has been diligently practicing and fine-tuning these symmetrical movements for several months. At four months, in prone, she supported herself on her forearms, beginning to extend her elbows. In practicing this action, she learns what her upper body can do. Between five and six months, babies also push from their hands and feet, to extend their knees and elbows. This month your baby may experiment by lifting her whole body up off the floor to a higher level in push-ups. These actions help your baby connect her upper body to her lower body.

Push-ups

Eye-foot coordination.

In play, babies enjoy slapping the floor with the palms of their hands. This activity provides them with the necessary stimulation so they can support their bodies on their hands. Like gymnasts performing a new balancing act, babies exercise balance and control by pushing and elevating their whole body up off the ground. They develop strength by supporting their weight on open hands and feet with toes tucked. While balancing in this position, a baby may turn around to look at her feet. This expands her visual range and develops her eye-foot coordination. Babies are learning to interact with the forces of weight, gravity, and balance to perform this dynamic action.

Note: the Adult Movement Exploration for push-ups is not included here. Because many adults have difficulty doing this movement effortlessly, push-ups are best explored with a movement educator.

Locomotion

When babies are on a smooth floor, they put the symmetrical push pattern into action by pushing with both hands and discover that their whole body slides backward. Babies often look puzzled or surprised when this happens because they are moving away from the direction they are trying to go, which is forward. Pushing away from an unpleasant situation is an essential protective skill that develops before the skill of advancing forward toward a person, toy, or object. Even while babies are exploring the symmetrical push patterns, they are preparing for the next locomotion pattern. Tucking their toes, flexing their ankles, and pushing with their feet prepare them for push off in belly crawling. Through exercising the pattern of one leg flexed and one leg extended, babies ready themselves for crawling, creeping, climbing, and walking. The exhilaration of exploring a new way of moving may lead to a baby combining vocalizing with the locomotion pattern.

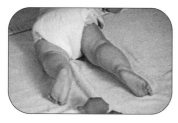

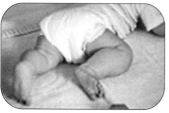

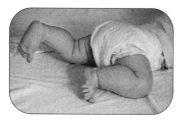

Pivoting in a circle, without rolling over.

112

Vocalizing in Motion Vignette

With both hands together, James pushes forward and his body slides backward. Practicing this action is a thrilling experience. James is fully grounded in his intent. We can see it in his movement and hear it in his percussive bellowing ah-ah-ah-ah. *James communicates his exhilarating experience through the power of his voice.*

This is dynamic body movement and James vocalizes for the duration of his pushing action. Through this action, the baby's spinal extension is counterbalanced with activation of abdominal support for the lumbar spine.

Vocalizing in Motion Vignette.

Adult Movement Explorations

Symmetrical Rocking: Hands and Feet

- Lie down in prone, support yourself on your forearms.
- Align your elbows under your shoulders, with your hands actively contacting the floor.
- Keep your pelvis in contact with the floor, with your legs extended, and tuck your toes.
- Push through your toes to produce a rocking motion.
- Alternately push from your hands and then push from your toes.
- Sense the interaction between your hands and feet.
- Pushing from your toes extends your knees.
- Repeat this a few times. Pause and extend your toes in between.
- Rest by rolling over onto your back, flex your knees, and keep your feet flat on the floor.

This is an excellent exercise for your whole foot, for toes, and especially your ankles. It is important to keep your feet and legs in a parallel position—make sure you don't lock your knees.

Changing Levels

- Look up at something that you find attractive, that is above you. Your visual focus will elevate your body to a higher level and provide the spinal support for your gaze.

- Push through your toes, allowing the movement to sequence through your body, simultaneously extending your knees and your elbows.

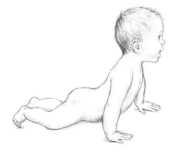

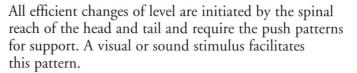

All efficient changes of level are initiated by the spinal reach of the head and tail and require the push patterns for support. A visual or sound stimulus facilitates this pattern.

Symmetrical Push Pattern: Locomotion

You will need a smooth floor such as wood or linoleum, but not ceramic tile.

- Lie down in prone, support yourself on your forearms, with your hands actively contacting the floor.
- Align your elbows under your shoulders.
- Keep your pelvis in contact with the floor, with your legs and toes extended.
- Gently push forward and downward with both hands, and feel your body slide backward. *(If you only push downward, but not forward at the same time, you will only elevate your shoulders and you will not slide.)*
- Slide your arms back to the beginning position.
- Align your elbows under your shoulders again.
- Allow the energy from the forward pushing action of your hands to travel backward down your spine all the way through your legs to your feet. Avoid the common tendency to let the action stop at your knees.
- Gently push downward and forward with both hands, and feel your body slide backward.
- Each time, you move an arm's length farther from the starting point.
- Repeat several times.
- Rest, by rolling onto your back with your knees flexed and feet flat.

The benefits of the symmetrical push patterns are
- *enhanced breathing*
- *suppleness and flexibility*
- *strength and coordination*

Energized by these movements, you will experience an increase in vitality that can help lessen fatigue and prevent lower back pain.

Moving farther and farther away from the toy.

115

Parent-Baby Interactions

Symmetrical Push Pattern

In the symmetrical push pattern position:

- Lie to the side of your baby or…
- Place yourself in front of your baby face-to-face.
- If your baby is pushing backward, you can also push backward and create more space between you and your baby.
- Next time you might add a sound like *ah-ah-ah* to your movement.

Your baby may enjoy this game and find the outcome of your action and the sound you make humorous. If your baby isn't enjoying this interaction, discontinue it and practice your movement explorations on your own. In your FloorPlay sessions with your baby, the emphasis is simply on sharing in the pleasure of moving, communicating, and learning together.

Losing Balance in Sitting

It will probably be another month before your baby comes to sitting by himself. When a baby is placed in the sitting position, he may show good stability with both legs flexed (ring sitting) for a brief period of time. With both arms free and a toy just beyond his reach, the six-month-old baby uses the forward protective extension response to get the toy. Holding his arms close to his body, he can wave and shake the toy about. However, in his excitement in waving it about, he can lose his balance. In the following vignette, while playing with his colorful doll, James' excitement gets the better of him and he topples over.

Toppling Over Vignette

James has been placed in the sitting position and he is holding on to a small rag doll. He transfers the doll hand to hand in a simultaneous grasp and release action. James reaches out using one hand for balance as he kicks his legs and vigorously waves and flings the little cloth doll about. While transferring the little rag doll hand to hand, James loses his balance and topples over. James' equilibrium responses are not fully developed in sitting yet, meaning that he can't break the fall by using his hand in a sideward protective extension response. James looks in the direction he is falling. He ends up on his side and then he rolls over onto his belly, wondering what happened!

His loss of balance as he topples over stimulates his righting reactions, and James rights his head as he rolls over into the prone position. Because James hasn't developed to independent sitting, he cannot return to sitting from the prone position. Six-month-old babies can protect themselves when they fall forward but protective extension responses to the side will not be present until the eighth month. Even though babies may have good stability when placed in the sitting position, it is only in independent sitting that they learn to coordinate their body to get there. From the sitting position they then learn to reverse the sequence to get back onto their hands and knees. You will learn more about how your baby coordinates his body to come to independent sitting next month.

Mark Johnson states in his book, *The Body in the Mind*, "We almost never reflect on the nature and meaning of balance, and yet without it our physical reality would be utterly chaotic…. The structure of balance is one of the key threads that holds our physical experience together as a relatively coherent and meaningful whole."

When babies are learning to move into the upright position, they develop protective extension responses called *equilibrium responses* for when they fall down to the ground. These begin to develop at six months and remain active throughout life. They are automatic patterns of response for maintaining balance when shifting one's center of gravity and base of support through space, from lying to sitting to standing.

Self-Directed Play

You will learn from the following episode why babies don't need to be overly stimulated or constantly entertained. When your baby sets up his own goal, he is exercising his capabilities in age-appropriate play to discover and arrive at his own solutions. These play sessions offer your baby an opportunity to experiment and practice his current movement skills and explore his problem-solving abilities to successfully complete his task. A good example is the following basket play episode. A number of questions are posed so you can marvel at the young baby's ingenuity.

Mouthing Toys

Colm begins his play session by mouthing a basket. Mouthing toys and objects is an essential part of your baby's self-directed play. When babies begin to play with a new toy, they first explore it with their mouths. Beginning with early feeding experiences, babies reach, grasp, release, and measure with their mouth. Recall Mara, at four months, grasping the yellow link with her mouth as well as her hands. Instead of just sucking on toys or objects, you may notice your baby is biting down and gnawing on firmer objects, one of the telling ways to know that she is teething. Through mouthing toys, babies learn about taste, texture, hardness, and the distinctive shapes of toys and objects. Six-month-old babies enjoy being in prone because this is a more functional play position. They are now learning to actively coordinate their mouthing explorations and their handling skills with a variety of body movements.

Babies reach, grasp, release, and measure with their mouths.

Babies learn about taste, texture, and shapes of objects.

118

Basket Play Vignette

Colm is playing with a basket. He increases the momentum of his arm to release his grip, and the basket rolls across the floor beyond his reach. He tries to get it. He pushes with his foot and this action elongates the side of his body just enough so that he can now reach and grasp the basket with his hand. (If you recall, we saw Gabrielle do this pattern at five months. This is one-half of the belly-crawling pattern seen next month).

Colm doesn't depend on vision to set up an action plan. Holding the basket in his right hand and without looking at what he is doing, he reaches down to his right side as far as he can toward his feet and lets go of the basket, and then he pivots his body around to get it.

Why did Colm let go of the basket if only to pick it up again? Is this a hiding game? Is he exercising his kinesthetic memory by not looking at what he is doing? Is it part of planning for an action response—reaching, letting go, remembering, and visually reaching to retrieve the basket? Do his actions reinforce "object permanence," or is it just the pure pleasure of moving his body in a new pivoting pattern to continue the game?

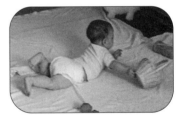

In this vignette, Colm is beginning to differentiate the sides of his body. Pivoting in prone provides babies with a new ability to shift weight on extended arms and reach to one side without rolling. If Colm were to repeat the action to the same side, he would end up pivoting in a whole circle. Colm is involved in a game and deliberately doesn't watch his action of placing the basket out of reach and out of sight—but *not out of mind!* There is a constant interplay here involving movement, mouthing, vision, and tactile development that has a direct impact on the coordination between perception and action.

By practicing this new movement, Colm knows he can pivot his body around and he anticipates that the basket will be there when he looks to the side to retrieve it. We

119

will observe another episode at twelve months when Mara drops a ball over her head while walking, and then turns to look for it. When babies create their own action plans, they discover or practice new movement skills that expand their present movement repertoire and enhance their learning experience.

Grasping and Handling Toys

In prone, six-month-old babies can shape their hands to toys or objects. They can use a palmar grasp for holding dowel-shaped objects, like the arms and legs of a doll. They are also refining their manual skills by using their thumb and fingers for separate functions. To grasp a larger object, they use their thumb to actively approach the object from the side so that their fingers can press the object against their thumb.

When a doll is the right size and shape for firm grasping, your baby may focus on what she wants to grasp and then uses this information to shape her hand. With a firm grip on the doll's foot or hand, babies can practice many large dynamic actions, such as banging, shaking, and swinging toys. Making an impact on her environment is such a thrilling experience that the baby's senses are keen and energized. Through this dynamic interplay, babies learn about their own actions, the properties of the toy they are playing with, and the sounds they can make. Some babies love to make loud sounds by slapping their open hands or banging toys on the floor.

As you tune in to the subtle nature of your baby's explorations, you will develop a new understanding of how your baby functions and learns. Watch and wonder at what your baby is doing and she will show you her unique and amazing accomplishments.

In Your Journal

You have many new movement sequences to explore this month that facilitate your breathing, body coordination, and movement awareness. You are learning new ways to organize your body. Using your whole body to interact with your baby as he grows will enhance your flexibility, coordination, and spontaneity in play.

These explorations will also increase your awareness of your baby's expanding locomotion skills. Share with others who take care of your baby your understanding of what has been important this month in your baby's actions, social interactions, and learning. Observe your baby's play with curiosity and interest—he just might share one of those smiles of self-mastery. Participate with pleasure in your own movement explorations and in being with your baby. It is a wondrous time when changes occur so quickly—enjoy every moment!

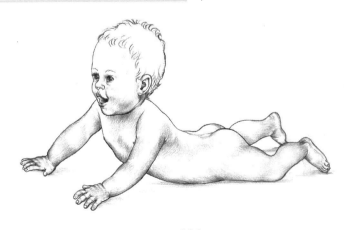

Six-Month Highlights

Movement Development and Learning

- Spinal Patterns
  - Flying like an airplane

- Symmetrical Patterns
  - Push-ups

- Lateral Patterns
  - Unilateral reaching
  - Pivoting in a circle

- Slapping open hand on floor
- Eye-foot coordination
- Visual-tactile-mouthing interplay
- Handling Explorations
  - Shaping hands to objects
  - Banging and shaking toys
  - Transferring toy hand to hand
  - Perceives texture, shape, and hardness of objects

Locomotion

- Spinal Patterns
  - Rolling

- Symmetrical Patterns
  - Pushing body backward

Spatial Awareness

- Symmetrical push backward on belly
- Changes levels in push-ups

Communication and Social Interactions

- Responds to own name
- Vocalizes with movement
- Watches other babies

Minds on the Move

Seven Months

In this lively locomotion stage, these busy little explorers can go where they want and get what they want. Your seven-month-old baby's desire is to move forward and up. Most babies have mastered rolling, push-ups, pushing backward, and pivoting in a circle. This month your baby adds two more locomotion patterns to her movement repertoire. For the first time, she can propel herself forward into the environment in a primitive belly-crawling mode to reach her goals. Before you know it, she will lift her belly off the ground and she will support her body on all fours. From the hands-and-knees position, your baby will come to independent sitting, will master getting in and out of sitting, and will start creeping on hands and knees.

Each change of level, position, and locomotion pattern offers your baby a variety of new movement possibilities in play and social interactions, expanding her scope for exploration and discovery of her environment. Your baby's evolving vertical orientation to gravity challenges her balance and equilibrium responses in these newly coordinated actions, as she learns to come to independent sitting and pull herself up to kneeling.

Crawling is a good example of "cognitive bootstrapping" in that busy brain. Bootstrapping is another term for the way brain growth leads to new experience and new experience unlocks more brain growth.

— Marian Diamond and Janet Hopson, *Magic Trees of the Mind*

At this stage, cross-lateral creeping offers your baby the largest scope for independent travel. From deliberate beginnings, this locomotion pattern transforms over the next few months. Before you know it, your baby will speed up her pace and be able to change directions. She will creep after a toy, pause, look around at something that has caught her interest, and then resume creeping. Watching her in action, you can almost see what areas of her brain are lighting up.

These few months are critical to your baby's motor development, so you'll want to make sure she has plenty of space in which to practice the movements of her arms and legs. Her vision is good enough to see a tiny boat from across the room or spy a toy red apple with a funny face smiling at her from the other side of the garden. Your baby's world is filled with tantalizing opportunities for play, and her natural curiosity moves her forward and upward toward her goals.

Developmental Movement

Your baby's body image is undergoing accelerated change as each new movement sequence is integrated into her nervous system. With her body supported on the floor, your baby has been learning to do push-ups, using both her hands and feet together; she has also been pushing with both hands to move her whole body across the floor. These symmetrical patterns help her to make connections between her upper and lower body and also to differentiate between them.

During this month, she gradually adds two new developmental movement patterns to her repertoire: a lateral (alternating sides) pattern and a cross-lateral (diagonal) pattern. Let's learn more about how these movement patterns unfold.

Note: crawling on hands and knees is technically known as creeping. Belly crawling says what it is, moving on the belly—a lateral push pattern. I use the word creeping for the hands-and-knees action—a cross-lateral pattern.

124

Lateral Push Patterns

This pattern begins with a lateral weight shift so that one side of the body is elongating as the other side of the body is flexing. One side of the body is supporting while the other side of the body is ready to move. When babies perform this pattern on alternate sides, they crawl forward on their bellies. Differentiating both sides of the body is important in the development of your baby's body image and learning. This development establishes a broad base for integrating both right- and left-sided functions.

Lateral push patterns differentiate the right side from the left side of the body, and vice versa.

Just as your baby is mastering one locomotion pattern, a situation may occur in the baby's environment that stimulates a new movement sequence. For example, if you are on the floor with your seven-month-old and you call your baby's name or attract your baby's attention by making a sound with a toy, he may shift his weight to one side and push with one hand to elongate one side of his body through to his foot. This action causes his body to curve in an arc so that he can turn to look at you.

Belly crawling is most often seen in the active seven-month-old who is intent on reaching a goal, such as grasping a colorful toy. Preceding belly crawling, babies begin with rapid, repetitive rocking on hands and knees, primarily in a forward/backward direction. Rocking stimulates many body systems:

- vestibular—inner-ear system that registers spatial orientation, velocity of movement, and balance;

- proprioceptive and kinesthetic receptors—skeletal-muscular system that registers the position of each part of the body in relation to the other parts, and where each part is in space.

Lateral push pattern, initiated from the hand.

If you feel tired or sluggish, try doing this movement and experience how much it energizes you. Your baby will delight in watching you explore this action.

Initiated from the hand.

From rapid, repetitive rocking on all fours, your baby will move back to the more familiar belly position. Focused on a colorful target, he flexes one leg and tucks his toes, and pushes off, elongating one side of his body through to the extended reach of his arm and hand on the same side. His opposite leg is free to flex and he can repeat this action on the other side of his body.

While some seven-month-olds do move through space in belly crawling, you may see this lateral push pattern only in the action of reaching for a toy performed by five- and six-month-olds. This reaching is one-half of the belly-crawling pattern. Looking at a toy or the cat across a room, your baby just might take off and begin crawling across the floor on his belly. By alternating sides, the full pattern opens up visual scanning in the diagonal field on either side of the midline. In this way visual scanning of the peripheral field is closely integrated with the baby's experience in belly crawling.

Suggestion: if it is summer when your baby is this age, spread a blanket out in the backyard or in a nearby park. You may notice your baby propel himself forward on his belly to reach for a flower or fluttering leaves, or to crawl after a pet.

Adult Movement Explorations

Lateral Push Pattern: Initiated from the Hand

On a smooth floor (not ceramic) you will slide easily, but a carpeted floor will be more comfortable and you will get a sense of the force traveling down each side of your body.

Note: be sure to keep both sides of your pelvis on the floor, encouraging lateral flexion without spinal rotation.

- Begin in the prone position, supported on your forearms, and shift your weight to the left side.
- Push more with your left hand and arm, and sense the force traveling through your left side to your foot.
- When you are on a smooth floor, one side of your body elongates in a convex curve and your body slides back.

126

- The tail end of your spine laterally flexes to the opposite side and releases the right half of your pelvis.
- This frees your right leg to flex so that you can now push off with your toes. See the following movement exploration.
- This is one-half of the belly-crawling pattern.
- For the second-half, repeat the pattern beginning with your right hand.
- Explore this movement a few times, on both sides.
- Rest by rolling over onto your back, flex your knees, and keep your feet flat on the floor.

Belly Crawling: Initiated from the Foot

Begin the exploration as above. If you have any back problems, simply explore this pattern to the point of flexing your leg on each side.

- Lie down in the prone position, supported on your forearms.
- Shift a little to the right and push with your right hand.

Rapid repetitive rocking on hands and knees often precedes belly crawling.

Lateral push pattern initiated from the foot.

- Sense the force traveling through your right side to your foot.
- The tail end of the spine laterally flexes to the left side, which releases your left pelvic half.
- This frees your left leg to be drawn up into full flexion, with the inner surface of your leg in contact with the floor.
- Tuck the toes of your flexed leg and push off.
- This will elongate the whole left side through to the left hand.
- Repeat on the other side to complete the belly-crawling cycle.

Independent Sitting

Independent sitting opens up a whole world for your baby, freeing his arms and hands. It's an eventful day when your baby comes to the sitting position by himself. Sitting upright for the first time involves new body coordinations so that your baby can change body levels: from prone to hands and knees, and then upright sitting. These actions challenge your baby's balance and equilibrium responses. To get there is a complex process, but he has the prerequisite skills to come to sitting by himself. Let's learn how Nels puts it all together.

Viewing the video sequence on the previous page, we see that Nels has been practicing lifting his belly up off the ground to get onto all fours. Once on hands and knees, he now adds rapid repetitive rocking, and when he sees a colorful toy on the other side of the garden, Nels quickly moves back down to prone and with a push from his foot, propels himself forward, belly crawling to reach it. From the prone position, Nels moves up onto his hands and knees again, then he reaches back with his pelvis to sit. He cautiously releases the support of one hand and only when he feels secure, does he slide the other hand to his body, freeing it from the ground. Nels looks up gingerly and smiles, sharing the pleasure of mastering this new skill. Then he is ready to move on to the next challenge that faces him: how to reverse the sequence to get back onto hands and knees. When trying this maneuver, babies often drop down to the stable belly position. When Nels has more experience in sitting, he will be able to bring both his hands together at the midline of his body to develop his functional and expressive skills.

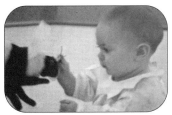

Buzzing Bee Vignette.

Buzzing Bee Vignette

Independent sitting opens up a whole world for the baby, freeing her arms and hands for new explorations. Mara's mother has a colorful yellow and black plushy bee puppet on her hand. She waves the bee about, making buzzing sounds. The colorful bee with gauzy, floppy wings captures Mara's attention and she waves her arms up and down, expressing her interest. The next time the bee comes close to her, Mara grasps and squeezes the bee's wing with both hands. Bringing her hands together in front of her body, she can now practice her gross and fine motor skills: Mara pulls the bee's wings and investigates the bee's antennae.

Cross-Lateral Patterns

When babies can move from hands and knees to sitting and get back onto all fours, they are ready to begin creeping. With their bodies suspended off the floor, babies can now develop a lightness of movement and quickness in timing, advancing their exploring skills. The diagonal patterns underlie the crossing of the midline of the body and coordinate the natural opposite arm and leg movements seen in both cross-lateral creeping and walking. Keep in mind, your baby is practicing many movement components and organizing her body in a variety of new ways. Although most babies begin to creep this month, there is no need for you to rush her. She may begin creeping at the end of the seventh month or she may not begin creeping until the eighth month. As with the development of any new skill, creeping efficiently is a

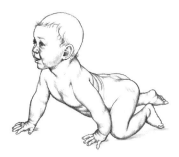

Cross-lateral patterns differentiate the diagonal pathway from the right arm to the left leg and from the left arm to the right leg.

129

Cross-lateral creeping initiated from the hand.

gradual process that takes several months to master. Your baby lifts her belly off the floor to change levels onto her hands and knees, then she transitions to sitting and learns to reverse the sequence to move back onto all fours, and now she is ready to begin creeping forward.

Creeping not only improves your baby's balance and body coordination but also reorganizes her perceptual experience. Endowed with a new level of versatility in movement, she covers more space expanding her perceptual scope to explore her world. For the first time, babies now function using three-dimensional movement. In this new movement pattern your baby uses a reach and pull action that begins from one hand. The reach and pull patterns add length and lightness to the body, so that babies can change levels easily and travel through space, increasing their speed over the next few months.

One day when your baby is attracted by a toy or pet, she will rise to the occasion and begin creeping after it. At the start, she may look a little awkward as she raises her belly off the floor. Balancing on her hands and knees, she reaches forward with one hand, pulling her opposite knee forward. Soon, with practice, this will be a synchronized, simultaneous action. When her right arm is lifted and her left leg is lifted off the ground, she precariously balances on her left arm and right leg. This diagonal connection is made through her body, coordinating her opposite arm and leg to move together.

From these deliberate beginnings, your baby will refine her creeping over several months. She will learn to start and stop with control, then without any prompting, she will speed up and take off for new horizons. She will slap the floor as she goes, delighting in the rhythmic sounds she makes. By the time she reaches eleven months, you will notice her accelerated timing and smoother rhythm in her creeping actions.

Creeping on hands and knees is the most sophisticated and elegant early locomotion pattern, a distinctly important stage of development. In this cross-lateral pattern, both sides of the body are coordinated to move with each other. Most movement specialists agree that this pattern, crossing the midline of the body, uses and integrates both halves of the brain. However, this cross-lateral integration is missing in creeping if the movement is initiated from the knee. In this case, all the weight is shifted laterally, resulting in the earlier unilateral (one-sided) pattern, but instead of being on the belly, the baby is now on hands and knees.

This integration is necessary for a variety of learning skills. Through this coordinated action, both eyes work together, and the ears develop in concert with each other. It has been noted by many developmental specialists that if a baby misses this important movement stage, it can lead to problems in sensory processing that will affect future development of reading and writing skills.

After gaining experience in creeping, babies may assume the side-lying position for play or to look at someone or something interesting. They can move from lying on their sides to hands and knees and, with more control in their creeping, they can pause to look around and then resume creeping.

If your baby isn't creeping on hands and knees yet, be patient; before you know it, she will enjoy the chase and catch game described next month. Keep in mind, as you read this book, that what is being described may be happening toward the end of the seventh month, whereas your baby may just be at the beginning of the seventh month.

Seven-month-old baby playing in side lying.

131

Adult Movement Explorations

Cross-Lateral Connection

You will become aware of the diagonal connection through the center core of your body, necessary for cross-lateral creeping.

- Lie down on the floor on your back.
- Flex your knees, place your feet flat on the floor, under your knees.
- Lift your left foot off the floor, bring your knee toward your upper body.
- Rest your left arm comfortably at your side.
- Place your right hand behind your head, resting your elbow on the floor.

- Exhale *la-la-la* and…
- Simultaneously lift your head and right arm up and look at your left knee. Do not pull your head with your hand, lift both effortlessly.

- Direct your elbow and opposite knee a little toward each other.
- Notice the diagonal pathway between your right arm and left leg.
- Lower your head and elbow to the floor and rest.
- Do this movement several times.
- When you have completed the movements, extend your legs and arms and rest.

Your head rotates naturally as you look at your opposite knee.

- Repeat the exploration with your right leg and left arm.

Cross-Lateral Variation

- Lie down on the floor in a large X-shape.
- Keep your right arm and left leg extended on the floor.
- Your left arm and right leg are flexed, with your right foot flat on the floor.
- Now lift your head and direct your left elbow and right knee toward each other; let your head and arm move freely. Notice there is more spinal rotation.
- Return to the large X-position, repeat with opposite arm and leg.

Spinal Reach and Pull Patterns

- Begin in the hands-and-knees position, with your hands on the floor directly under your shoulders and your knees directly under your hips.
- Keep the width between your shoulder blades.
- Push with your hands but keep them in the same place.
- Lead the movement with your tailbone (spinal reach of the tail) to sit on your heels.
- Your toes are extended and flat on the floor.
- Lead the movement with your head (spinal reach of the head) to return to hands and knees.
- Explore a few times, ending up sitting on your heels with your hands on the floor.

Initiated from the tail.

Initiated from the head.

133

Do this experiment and decide where this movement is initiated from.

Now try an experiment to decide if your spine shortens or lengthens.

- Beginning in the hands-and-knees position, initiate the movement from your lumbar region (back of waistline) to sit back on your heels.
- Now starting again from the hands-and-knees position, actively push through your hands and reach with your tailbone to sit back on your heels.

In which movement do you experience your spine as longer? If you can't decide, explore each movement several times.

- Your spine is shorter and rounded when you initiate the movement with the back of your waistline (lumbar region).
- Your spine is lengthened when you initiate the movement from the reach of your tailbone.
- Align your head with your spine all the way to your tailbone.

Note: after the spinal reach and pull patterns are established, they provide the lightness for the reach and pull patterns from the arms and legs.

Cross-Lateral Creeping

When a visual or sound stimulus captures your baby's attention, her curiosity or attention directs her to move toward it. Maybe she heard you call her name or she sees a colorful toy on the other side of the room.

- Begin in the hands-and-knees position, with your hands on the floor directly under your shoulders and your knees directly under your hips.
- Look around the room and focus on something of interest.
- Now move toward it, reaching out with your hand.
- As you transfer your body weight forward, feel the opposite knee move forward.
- Sense the diagonal pull sequencing through your body, connecting opposite arm and leg.

- Repeat this movement by alternating sides to complete the cross-lateral creeping cycle.

Continue creeping around the room until you establish a steady rhythm.

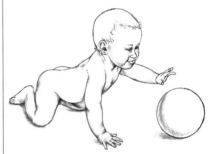

Private Practice

In my private practice and public workshops, I have worked with many adults, adolescents, and children who have not fully integrated this stage of development. When we are exploring this movement sequence, a number of participants are surprised to find they automatically creep in a unilateral pattern. It has been found that some adults with lower-back problems, because of the lack of spinal rotation, creep in a unilateral pattern by initiating the movement with a push from their knee instead of

Mara adjusts her body as she pulls up to kneeling and discovers how far she is from the floor.

reaching with their hand. If the unilateral creeping pattern is dominant, sensory processing is occurring on the same side of the body. Therefore, there is no communication between the two brain hemispheres, which may lead to inefficient sensory processing, and stressful learning patterns.

Changing an inefficient movement pattern to an effortless graceful sequence is called *repatterning*. I have found that some participants, when repatterning a unilateral creeping pattern to a more integrated cross-lateral movement pattern, may temporarily experience dizziness and a sense of imbalance. Remember this pattern activates both hemispheres of the brain simultaneously. However, with practice, this new cross-lateral pattern will soon become rhythmic, effortless, and smooth. In cross-lateral creeping, babies activate both sides of their brain. Such brain activation prepares them to integrate complex ideas and fine-tunes the adult's body-mind integration, improving clarity of thinking.

Kneeling

This month, your baby can pull herself up to kneeling by holding on to a ledge or a piece of furniture. Aligning her body with the furniture requires subtle knee adjustments before she can balance herself while kneeling. Your baby then measures the space with her hands, from the ledge down to the floor, to discern how near or how far she is from the ground. The information that she receives from her hands, from visually surveying the spatial layout of her surroundings, and from monitoring her movements contributes to her developing body-confidence. Moving upward is a balancing act between stability and mobility, and your baby's split-second postural adjustments indicate she is able to control her movements and anticipate the outcome of her actions during the process of pulling herself up to kneeling, so that she successfully completes the action.

In Your Journal

This month has been active for both you and your baby. Your new movement explorations will enhance your spinal awareness, activate muscles on both sides of your body, strengthen your back, and stimulate your brain. If you need to calm down, remember to do your breathing explorations, or rest on your back in the knees-up position and breathe easily. If you need an energizer, try the symmetrical yield and push pattern in Chapter 4, or this month's rapid repetitive rocking on hands and knees. Take time to note your experience, what changes you are aware of, and how much better you feel as you expand your movement repertoire.

Write down what your baby enjoys this month. Pictures of you and your baby on the floor together will be precious reminders of your time moving and learning together in this dynamic locomotion stage.

Seven-Month Highlights

Movement Development and Learning
- Pulling up to kneeling
- Rocking on hands and knees
- Independent sitting
  – Hands free for exploration
- Protective extension forward
- Handling Explorations
  – Banging and shaking toys

Locomotion
- Lateral Patterns
  – Unilateral push backward
  – Belly crawling

- Cross-Lateral Patterns
  – Creeping on hands and knees

Spatial Awareness
- Unilateral push backward and belly crawling
- Changes levels
  – Creeping on hands and knees
  – Sitting
  – Kneeling

Communication and Social Interactions
- Smiles to share mastery
- Baby recognizes own name
- Watches other babies

Actions before Words

8

Eight Months

Eight-month-old babies take great pleasure in their newfound mode of travel, creeping on hands and knees. Gradually, and with much practice over the next few months, they refine this locomotion pattern to move with increasing speed and in a smoother rhythm.

Can you believe how quickly your baby has become so mobile? In the pre-locomotion stage he explored moving his body only within his personal space, defined by the reach of his arms and legs. In the initial locomotion stage, on a smooth floor, your six-month-old baby learned to push himself with both hands so that his whole body slid backward. Focused on a colorful toy, your seven-month-old propelled himself forward to reach his target. Now, with his belly off the ground, he is moving at a higher level, and a new tantalizing environment entices your curious eight-month-old baby to go farther afield. Just for the sheer joy of moving his body, he creeps everywhere, exploring his surroundings. During this month you will learn more about how these locomotion patterns relate to your baby's developing functional skills and expressive actions.

Physical movement, from earliest infancy and throughout our lives, plays an important role in the creation of nerve cell networks which are actually the essence of learning.

—Carla Hannaford,
Smart Moves

Sitting independently creates the freedom of movement for your baby to use his arms and hands for expanded discovery in play. He will become more adept at picking up and handling smaller toys and objects. A significant event this month is that he can voluntarily release a toy in one of several different ways. His new ability of rotating his forearm lets him explore three-dimensional objects, which further enhances his perceptual development. In his social interactions, you will learn how your baby expresses himself and interprets the body language of those around him. Before words, he adds new postures and gestures to his repertoire and expresses himself effectively through his recently acquired body language.

At the top of your baby's agenda is his ability to elevate his body and change body levels in bear standing, kneeling, and pulling himself up to supported standing. Delighting in this new perspective of his environment, he must also learn to get back down to the floor again.

Movement Is Functional and Expressive

By closely observing your baby's movement and also doing the movements yourself, you have gained an experiential understanding of how these movement patterns develop. In the locomotion stage, you learned how your baby puts these patterns into motion so that she quickly learns how to interact with her environment. In Part One you were also introduced to the four basic actions that combine to make up the developmental movement patterns. Now, let's expand further to discover how the combination of two or more of these four basic actions form the foundation for developing "increasing and decreasing pressure" in your baby's functional and expressive actions. Once again, described below, they are *yielding, pushing, reaching,* and *pulling.*

Yield and Push are patterns of *compression* that develop through one's relationship to *gravity*. In these patterns, babies yield to connect with the force of gravity and develop strength by pushing their whole body weight against the resistance of gravity.

Reach and Pull are patterns of *elongation* that develop through one's relationship to *space*. In these patterns, babies focus and reach outward, developing streamlined mobility and lightness to change body levels and explore new frontiers of space in their environment.

Locomotion and the Environment

To understand how your baby combines these actions, let's look in more detail at the following locomotion patterns. With practice you can recognize where your baby's *focus* of attention is, where the movement is *initiated* from, how the action *sequences* through the body, and in what *direction* your baby moves.

Symmetrical Patterns

Six-month-old babies push with both hands and discover that their bodies slide *backward*, away from the beginning point. You can see babies push from both their hands and their feet to raise their body off the ground in body push-ups. Babies develop strength by moving their whole body weight against the resistance of gravity.

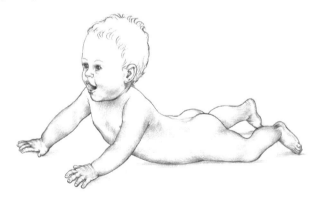

Lateral Patterns

Seven-month-old babies propel themselves *forward* into the environment. This lateral pattern occurs as babies shift their weight to one side. Directing their intent to reach a toy, babies push with one foot so that the force elongates the same side of the body into a reach with the hand.

141

To reach their goal, babies alternate sides to move through space in belly crawling.

Cross-Lateral Patterns

Eight-month-old babies direct their intent to change spatial levels and with streamlined mobility creep in a cross-lateral (hands-and-knees) pattern. Babies reach forward with one hand and a diagonal connection is made through the body, pulling the opposite leg forward. Here, with minimal body contact on the floor, babies balance on one hand and the opposite knee. In this pattern the movement is freer and lighter, giving babies the ability to increase speed beyond what was possible in belly crawling.

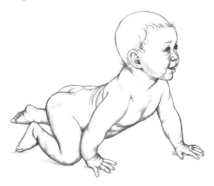

Movement Variations

Through his actions, your baby learns to vary the elements of *focus, pressure, timing*, and *flow* of his movement. A few examples will help to make this clearer.

He can vary his *focus* of attention while scanning his surroundings, and then make a beeline across the room to something that attracts him, or zero in on the tiniest object nearby. Your baby also learns to vary the *pressure* he applies to his actions. To increase pressure, he exerts more force or greater strength as he slaps the floor with an open hand. To decrease pressure, he lightens his body contact or applies a lighter touch, for example, when he reaches out to touch your face. Curious about his environment, the already mobile baby moves through space on his hands and knees and, over the next few months, improves his *timing* and *flow.* He learns to creep in a quicker *rhythm* and with more fluidity in a *smoother* action. Also, with increasing agility, as we shall soon see, he can quickly slide his hand into a basket to get a soft toy before the lid closes. In illustrated examples, you will learn how the eight-month-old baby incorporates these movement elements in his functional actions and expressive communication.

Independent Sitting

While some babies may sit independently for the first time this month, other babies may have already developed the ability to sit up and play with toys, using a variety of body positions. When playing with a toy, babies may sit with both legs flexed (ring sitting). Although this is a stable position, it prevents a baby from shifting her weight to change her body position. You may also see babies who sit with both legs extended. As you might expect, your baby will soon combine both these two positions, sitting with one leg flexed and the other leg extended.

Developing equilibrium responses in a protective extension response to the side (she reaches out with her arm to prevent falling), your baby illustrates her balance and mobility when she transitions in and out of a variety of sitting positions.

Independent sitting also makes it possible for babies to use their arms and hands to communicate with new

When losing their balance, babies reach forward or to the side to keep from falling.

143

gestures, expanding their body language repertoire. When babies can move among a variety of sitting positions, their body postures become available to them to communicate an array of expressions. In her book, *As Others See Us*, movement analyst Ellen Goldman informs us, "The whole body, arms, legs, hands, back and feet are arranged in a configuration which projects a mood or feeling: '*I am tired*,' can be seen in a drooping body, or, '*I am listening attentively*,' seen as a focused, alert body. The posture sets the mood." The following vignette of two eight-month-old babies provides a clear example.

Red Ball and Little Boat Vignette

Mara sits and watches Gabrielle playing with a small toy. What does her body posture tell us? We notice the quality of Mara's sitting, her effortless body alignment, her calm composure, and her receptive, attentive focus. We do not have to see the expression on her face since her body alignment and posture communicate more than words can say! We can surmise and almost hear her saying, "I am curious and interested in what Gabrielle is doing." Meanwhile, Gabrielle, while playing with a little boat, looks over at Mara. Gabrielle may be acknowledging that she knows Mara is watching what she is doing. Mara may be focusing specifically on Gabrielle's new hand skill (she can rotate her forearm to look at the top, side, and bottom of the little boat) or she may be watching how Gabrielle can release the boat in a variety of ways. Whatever action captures Mara's attention, she waves and flaps her arms up and down excitedly, expressing her delight.

Gabrielle drops the boat on the floor and Mara quickly retrieves it. Then, Mara deliberately releases the red ball but, before Gabrielle can grasp it, she gets it again. In close proximity to each other, Mara and Gabrielle skillfully maneuver their arms and hands, learning to successfully interact with each other. Mara ends the play session with a squeal of delight, then she creeps away.

144

Handling Skills

Being able to attain new levels in independent sitting and the ability to transition in and out of a variety of sitting positions offers new opportunities for your baby to develop her handling skills in play. These achievements enable your baby to use both hands to investigate small toys and objects. If you recall, at four months, Mara could use only a pulling action to release a chain of links from her hand. At six months, James could use a simultaneous grasp-and-release action to transfer a little cloth doll from hand to hand.

During the eighth month, there are three significant handling developments:

- increasing pressure to maintain a firm grip on a toy,
- decreasing pressure to voluntarily release a toy,
- rotating the forearm to look at all three sides of a toy or object.

Researchers Emily Bushnell and Paul Boudreau define the term *haptic* perception as "the ability to acquire information about objects with the hands, to discriminate and recognize objects from handling as opposed to just looking at them." In their article, "Motor Development and the Mind," they add, "…the visual information related to an object's 3-D structure is especially clear and accessible when the object is viewed while held and maneuvered in the hand…. In other words, infants must be able to execute the specified motor abilities in order for the corresponding perceptual abilities to emerge." Handling skills propel your baby's learning to a new cognitive level. With their increasing ability to focus on the task at hand, babies can now anticipate the outcome of their actions. For example, by banging two blocks together, babies can associate the size and shape of the toys and their ability to make different kinds of sounds, depending on how far apart they hold the blocks, the amount of pressure they use, and the quickness of rhythmic contact.

The following descriptive illustrations will help you to better understand this functional development.

145

Functional Actions

Babies can now direct their functional actions to achieve a cognitive goal with an anticipated outcome.

Blocks are better than balls for these manual skills and handling explorations.

The eight-month-old baby uses a variety of hand grasps, adjusting both her grasp and its pressure to the shape of the toy or object.

Babies develop precision when matching two surfaces and banging two blocks together to make sounds.

The eight-month-old baby's hands meet at midline to bang two blocks together. This action is a precursor to future functional skills, for example, a baby varies pressure when playing a variety of musical toy instruments.

146

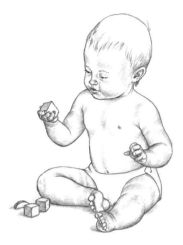

Babies must be able to rotate their forearm before the corresponding perceptual abilities emerge.

The eight-month-old baby can hold on to a toy, rotate (pronate/supinate) her forearm to look at the top, side, and bottom of the toy. This action also prepares a baby to use a spoon to feed herself.

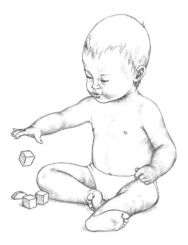

Once babies can voluntarily release a toy they will enjoy dropping objects in containers.

The eight-month-old baby releases toys in a variety of ways. The action of decreasing pressure to release one's grip is necessary for a variety of functional and manipulation skills. A baby now can release a toy so that he can grasp and pick up another one.

Adult Movement Explorations

Diagonal Connection

Place a folded towel under your head if needed.

- Lie down on your back. Sense the alignment of your spine, head-to-tailbone.
- Place your legs parallel, flex your knees, and position your feet in full contact with the floor.
- Extend your arms horizontally to the side, slightly lower than your shoulders, palms up and hands active.
- Exhale *la-la-la*, and lower your legs to the right side.
- Notice that the outside of your right foot and the inside of your left foot contact the floor.
- Notice that your legs don't stay together.
- Rest your legs, and breathe easily.
- During this gradated spinal rotation, your left arm may move up a little on the floor.
- Notice a diagonal connection from your right knee through your torso to your left arm.
- Exhale *la-la-la* to return to your midline position. As your tailbone moves toward the floor, notice the deepening in your hip joints.
- Repeat to the left side.

Explore a few times to each side.

Protective Extension

Exploring your own protective responses will help you to recognize them when your baby does them. They develop forward, sideward, and then backward. These equilibrium responses that are gravity-oriented remain part of our adult repertoire.

- Kneel-sit on your heels.
- Rest your hands lightly on your thighs, ready to move.
- Slowly lean *forward* as if you were going to fall. Wait until both your hands automatically reach out to break

the fall, protecting you by contacting the floor (develops at 7 months).

- Remain in kneel-sitting or sit in the ring position—try both.
- Lean to the right side until your right hand reaches out to protect you from falling over. Do this to the left side as well (develops at 8 months).
- Now begin in the ring sitting position.
- Slowly lean *backward*, preparing to fall, and wait until your hands reach backward to catch you (develops at 9 to 10 months).

Note: when your baby develops these protective responses backward, she can turn and transition from sitting to hands and knees. You will learn to do this in the following exploration.

Sitting to Hands and Knees

This exploration improves rhythmic flow, timing, and spatial awareness in the transitions from sitting to hands and knees.

- Begin in the ring sitting position.
- Legs are semi-flexed, and the soles of the feet are in contact with one another.
- Hands lightly contact the floor at your sides.

- Look to your left; shift your weight to sit on your left hip, and release your right hand.
- Continue turning onto hands and knees.
- Look to your left again; shift your weight to sit on your right hip, and release your left hand.

- Continue turning toward the left to the ring sitting position, facing the direction you began.
- You can continue moving in a line to the left or change direction and move to the right.
- With each complete sequence you have faced all four directions.

Follow the movement instructions and use the photographs as a guide.

149

- This activity develops ease in shifting your body weight into different positions in a flowing motion. With practice, you will learn to coordinate your legs to fold and unfold with ease.

Supported Standing

Your baby experiences a dramatically different perspective of her environment as she experiments with changes of level from creeping, to kneeling, to pulling up to standing. When babies first pull themselves to standing, they use both feet together, wobbling on their toes before lowering themselves onto their whole foot. A more experienced baby can support herself on one foot in a half-kneeling position and push down on a ledge with both hands to come to standing. Once in the standing position, babies can turn their bodies to use one hand for support and lower themselves to the floor to pick up a toy. Reaching down to pick up a toy, a baby will counterbalance her free arm by extending her opposite leg to position her foot for more control and stability. In this dynamic position, her feet are active, making moment-to-moment adjustments anticipating her changing posture so that she maintains her balance while completing the action of grasping and picking up the toy. These developments of responsive feet and flexed ankles and toes are precursors for push-off in independent walking.

Bear Standing

At seven or eight months, your baby may elevate and support her whole body on hands and feet in the position called "bear standing." Demonstrating her increased leg mobility to assume this position, your baby places her hands under her shoulders and her feet directly under her hips. The nine-month-old baby develops the skill to put this pattern into motion in "bear walking," as you will discover next month when you explore this dynamic movement along with your baby.

Creeping Enhances Social Interaction

Creeping enhances your baby's social interactions and play explorations in her environment. With more control of her body in motion, she is ready for more active social involvement. When parents play on the floor at the baby's level, they will know the right moment at which to engage with their baby in a chase and catch game. When you and your baby are on hands and knees and your baby is actively focused on you, you can begin creeping away — she will get the idea and creep after you. Let her grab and hold on to your clothing to catch you. You will hear your baby's love for this locomotion game in her joyful laughter and squeals of delight.

In *Emotion and Its Regulation in Early Development*, infant researchers Joseph Campos, Rosanne Kermoian, and Marcia Zumbahlen reinforce what most parents have noticed: once their baby reaches the creeping stage, their infant's play is more interactive, defined in terms of games like peekaboo or chase. They report, "The changes in interactive play reported for locomotor infants are significant for several reasons: The infants seemed to be initiating the games, the games involved more than one person, the infant's partner was often not the mother but rather the father, a sibling, or a pet, and the games had simple rules that involved turn taking. The games were also usually marked by high levels of positive affect by both the infant and the social partner. …the glee associated with the high arousal produced by the games was much more prevalent among crawling [creeping] infants."

Baby and mother delight in a chase and catch game.

Parent-Baby Interactions

Chase and Catch Game

If your baby wasn't creeping last month, you probably didn't play a chase and catch game. This month, if she is sitting independently and already creeping, you may be able to add this to your FloorPlay.

- Begin by sitting on a carpeted floor together.
- Assume the hands-and-knees position.
- When your baby is actively focused on you, creep a short distance away, then turn around to look at her.
- If your baby is interested, she will get the idea and creep after you.
- With gleeful anticipation, the speed of her creeping will increase as she tries to catch you.
- Let your baby catch you by grasping your clothes or touching you.

Though this action, babies gain body-confidence when all parts of their body move in rhythmic coordination.

Nonverbal Communication

In our social interactions, we tune in at an intuitive level to the unspoken messages that ring loud and clear. These nonverbal messages are called *body language*. We could also define body language as the meaning in our expressive movements. These nonverbal messages may override what a person is actually saying, especially if the listeners perceive that the person's body language and vocal tone don't match the verbal message. Over the years, many nonverbal communication researchers have studied adult body language in different forms—gestures, postures, facial expression, eye movement, vocal tone, and rhythmic dialogues. These studies show just how important the nonverbal component is for authentic communication. That's why babies are such a joy as they communicate what they mean through their whole body expression.

Preverbal Communication

The origins of our adult nonverbal communication are rooted in the baby's preverbal behavior during the first year of life. Babies learn to both express and interpret expressive body language long before they communicate in words. By the time a baby is eight months old, she can express herself through a variety of independent sitting postures, expressive gestures, or gestures plus vocalization. By the time they are twelve months old, most babies combine gestures with one or two words and an action. In this preverbal stage, the babies' gestures and postures continue to expand their body-language repertoire to enhance their communication ability, which will enrich the meaning of their words when they reach the toddler stage.

Although all babies are similar in what they are developing and experiencing at each stage, what they communicate about and how they communicate it are unique. Each baby's gestures, postures, and vocalizations are individual— a special way of expressing herself. Whether it be a quizzical look, a high-octave squeal, a determined helping hand, an encouraging pat on the head, or a curious, attentive posture, there is no mistaking your baby's signature expressions.

Well before entering the toddler stage, babies have developed patterns of movement and expressive gestures and postures to effectively interact in any new situation. These unspoken messages guide your baby's social interactions, helping her accurately assess whether situations are comfortable or uncomfortable. Now that she is more familiar with most people's responses in her immediate surroundings, she is becoming better equipped to interpret the nonverbal behavior that accompanies all personal communication and social interactions. Your independent baby will pay close attention to both your body language and your tone of voice to comprehend the meaning in your "verbal messages." The following illustrated actions will help you to observe the development of your baby's expressive preverbal communication.

153

Expressive Communications

Babies communicate effectively through their expressive postures and gestures.

Postures are the unified expression of the whole body projecting a mood or a feeling.

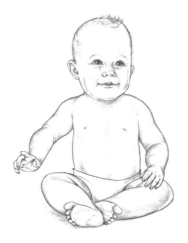

Eight-month-old babies communicate poise, curiosity, interest, and confidence through their body posture.

Babies are mastering the preverbal communication that will later accompany their words.

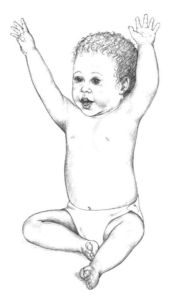

Babies can now raise both arms up overhead to wave and show their delight. Soon your baby will learn to wave one hand at a time meaning "goodbye."

154

Gestures are movements of individual parts of the body separately or in combination, expressive of a feeling, thought, or idea.

By eight months of age, babies increase pressure in clapping their hands together to express their pleasure.

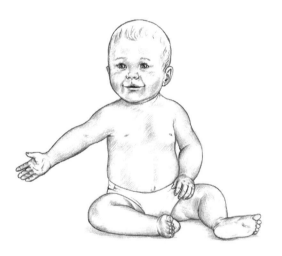

Soon your baby's gestures will accompany a sound and by her first birthday she may use an action, gesture, and word together.

Babies can rotate their forearm, elbow extended with palm up, to express their encouragement. You might use this simple hand movement to invite your baby to do something.

155

Baby-to-Baby Dialogues

In peer play, what experiences do babies communicate about at eight months? Certainly they communicate their delight in their current physical learning, that is to pull themselves up to a new level in supported standing, and to reach down to pick up a toy from this position. Babies also want to communicate with other babies, and they enjoy just watching them exploring and handling toys. When your baby is thrilled at what she is observing, you just might see a new gesture spring forth. Babies also watch other babies' faces as they listen intently to their vocalizations. In their peer interactions, babies are curious about the sounds they are hearing, the expressive gestures they are seeing, and the touch they are feeling. They learn to put it all together to understand and respond to the other baby's message. These significant events are at the center of their shared experience.

In these preverbal dialogues, these babies express themselves succinctly through all the human capacities available to them before words: focus, body movement, touch, and vocalizing. Babies communicate their feelings and needs more precisely through their movement patterns, body postures, and variety of gestures.

Your baby's expressive movement repertoire is not just a precursor of language development that is replaced by verbal development. This expressive body language is the nonverbal component that underlies all communication, social interactions, and expressive dialogues for babies and adults alike. Babies not only learn to interpret these unspoken messages in social interactions, but also to develop their own communication style, their unique expression.

The following vignette provides us with a deeper understanding of how one baby comprehends another baby's motivation, and how she tries to help her reach her goal.

Roots of Empathy Vignette

Mara is kneeling with her hands on a ledge beside Gabrielle, who has already pulled herself up to supported standing. The change of level to supported standing offers a change of perspective. With more experience in standing, Gabrielle anticipates Mara's desire to reach the same level. Gabrielle bangs the ledge and vocalizes her encouragement. You could imagine her saying, "Come up here. You can do it!" From the kneeling position, Mara looks up at Gabrielle, who looks down at her; then they grasp and hold hands. Their joint attention, mutual intent, and spatial interaction create a basis of understanding and a way to communicate. Gabrielle not only understands Mara, she wants to help her!

Gabrielle tries to help Mara by pulling on her sweater. Mara acknowledges Gabrielle's encouragement by her attentive focus and hand grasp. Mara is ready to venture up to this new level, and her unwavering focus helps her reach her goal as she gradually pulls herself up to standing.

Roots of Empathy Vignette.

Babies are building a rich, expressive nonverbal vocabulary. In an already existing social environment, they skillfully maneuver the complex world of adult behavior and learn to interpret the nonverbal messages around them. Babies cue into subtle nuances of mood to form impressions of people and situations. This ability lets babies evaluate a situation, choose when to initiate an interaction and when to redirect their playful intent. In his book, *The Growth of the Mind*, Stanley Greenspan comments, "With the same simple yet subtle gestural signals that defined our very earliest interactions, we will negotiate all our relationships as long as we live."

The roots of our adult nonverbal expression sprout from these subtle beginnings. Our expressive body language amplifies our words. Gestures serve a variety of functions; they support our words and lend vitality to our verbal message. Gestures don't always follow one after the other;

in conversation two or more gestures may emerge simultaneously. Nor do gestures occur in isolation; rather, they are natural responses to the body posture we assume and it is our posture that expresses our attitude or mood in the context of any given situation. Ellen Goldman, in *As Others See Us,* states, "Whereas gestures establish and keep the beat between people, giving a coherent rhythm to communication, postures support communication and establish a common platform of meaning." She continues, "In an Integrated Movement, the same quality of movement has to travel through the posture and gesture."

This is the missing piece of the puzzle to understanding the unspoken messages expressed by body language. Whenever communication is accompanied by an appropriate action, for example, an uproarious laugh to an amusing situation, we perceive that person's expression to be genuine. What is actually occurring in this particular situation is the merging of posture and gesture. It is this synthesis that conveys a true response. These kinds of genuine responses that your baby experiences in her relationship with you help her to distinguish the difference between natural, authentic communication and the superficial gestures she may encounter in others.

Although it will be several years before your baby's actions are backed up by clear intention in more complex social interactions, you may already be starting to see the roots of her disposition. As an example, you may have heard yourself say about your baby, "She's so determined." If you have, then you are already tuning in to one of her motivating preferences for action!

In Your Journal

By organizing your body in new ways and exploring more dynamic movements, you are stimulating your nervous system to its peak functioning. Your new exploration this month, moving from hands and knees to sitting, may take some practice before you can coordinate your body to do it smoothly. When you explore these movement patterns, can you sense the action sequencing through your body?

Are you able to recognize the actions of yield and push from reach and pull in your baby's locomotion patterns? Can you see how your baby maintains a firm grip on a toy by increasing pressure? Do you recognize this in her expressive actions when she bangs her hand up and down to get your attention? Add any other special experiences you observe.

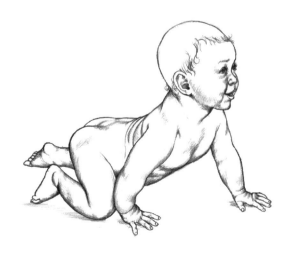

Eight-Month Highlights

Movement Development and Learning
- Ring, half-ring, long, and half-long sitting
- Bear standing
- Supported standing
- Protective extension sideways
- Handling Explorations and Skills
  - Rotates forearm to see all sides of a toy
  - Voluntary release of toys
  - Banging two blocks together
  - Fine motor: lateral pinch
  - Perceives three-dimensional shape of an object

Locomotion
- Cross-Lateral Patterns
  - Creeping on hands and knees

Spatial Awareness
- Changes levels
  - Sitting
  - Bear standing
  - Climbing
  - Supported standing and squatting

Communication and Social Interactions
Baby-Parent
  - Looks, touches, vocalizes
  - New postures and gestures
  - Chase and catch game

Peer play
  - Looks, touches, vocalizes
  - New postures and gestures
  - Object play

160

Timing in Action

Nine Months

You may find it hard to keep up with your baby this month. No longer confined to a single room, your curious nine-month-old can now reach the knobs on those inviting cabinets and low drawers. You will discover her having a delightful time banging the pot lids together. Outdoors, you might find her chasing after a neighbor's cat, charging through a pile of leaves, or sitting quietly picking up a leaf using her newly acquired pincer grasp. Inside and outside, the world invites your curious nine-month-old baby to explore and investigate. Suddenly she can satisfy her curiosity by going where she wants to get what she wants.

You may notice that your baby's creeping is speeding up as she actively moves from place to place in a whirl of activity. She knows that you aren't far away and that for those special moments of reassurance she can quickly turn back to you. You may also notice an improved sense of rhythmic timing in her creeping, vocalizing, and reaching. Babies at this age are practicing their fine motor and handling skills. At this time, you may enjoy playing a fun game of catch with your baby, using a small soft ball.

By late infancy or early childhood, sequences of skilled movements have developed and can be repeated or shifted from their usual place in a sequence. Furthermore, children have learned how to signal their playful attitude more clearly.

— Catherine Garvey, *Play*

From the sitting position babies can aim and throw a small ball overhand with increasing accuracy, within a short distance. Still, be ready to jump up and get that ball wherever it goes.

Your baby feels so big now as she moves up to supported standing. Once she is on both feet, she must rebalance and adjust her body to meet her new verticality. Now, the challenge is how to get down! Initially, your baby may just fall or try sinking to the floor. With practice, her knees will flex so she can squat down, then extend as she pulls herself up with her hands. With their newfound locomotion this month, babies put all their movements into practice, exploring a new bear-walking pattern and climbing up a set of stairs or up a grassy hill. From creeping to climbing to cruising, your baby takes delight in her ability to change levels and look at her surroundings from different perspectives.

Climbing

Now when your baby sees the stairs, she moves quickly to navigate new territory and explore her environment further. Climbing upward is a challenge, and climbing upward occurs before climbing down. If you have a short staircase of only two or three stairs and your baby has climbed to the top, she will probably try to climb down headfirst, so keep your eye on her. Next month, you will learn more about how babies get down from higher places. In the following interaction, you can encourage your baby to climb up and over your legs.

Parent-Baby Interactions

Climbing Up and Over

- Sit on the floor with your legs in an open V-position.
- Noticing your new body position, your baby will probably creep toward you.
- You can also call her, "(Baby's name), do you want to climb up and over my legs?"

162

- Once she climbs over, you can entice her to climb behind you and creep to the other side.
- If she climbed over your left leg, attract her with a toy in your opposite right hand and hold it behind your back, so she can still see or hear it.
- When you notice her moving toward it, slowly move your hand so she continues creeping around you to the other side.
- Place the toy between your legs.
- She will probably climb up and over your right leg to get the toy and sit between your legs.

Variation: you can sit on the floor with both your legs extended together so that your baby can climb over both your legs.

Protective stepping response in baby in background.

Supported Standing

If a baby's center of gravity is displaced, she will reach back and stamp her foot to regain her balance (protective stepping response). In supported standing, she will then step to the side to widen her base of support. In independent standing, the baby will step out with her leg in the direction of the fall to catch herself, with options to step forward, sideways, backward, or diagonally.

Cruising

Using one hand for support, increased spinal rotation allows babies to turn around to scan their surroundings. Seeing a toy at the other end of a bench, your baby may walk sideways (cruising) to get it. Her hands and feet move in synchrony with each other as she rhythmically combines walking hands with side stepping. If she wants to play with a toy in this position, she will lean her body against a piece of furniture for support, so she can free both hands for play. Taking steps sideward in cruising promotes good foot alignment when practiced to each side. Using one hand for support while practicing rotation is a transition from using both hands in cruising to using one hand for support in forward walking.

Cruising.

163

Bear walking through the grass.

Bear Walking

At six months, your baby did push-ups by tucking her toes and extending her elbows to support herself on hands and toes. After mastering this position, your active seven- or eight-month-old progressed to pushing up onto her hands and feet in the bear-standing position. With her legs tucked under her pelvis, she extends her legs and stands on her whole foot while supporting herself on her hands. This ability requires both pelvic stability and good shoulder-girdle control. At nine months your baby can shift her weight to bear walk in a cross-lateral pattern across the room or outside. Babies often bear walk when they are outside on a grassy or rocky terrain because they may not like the feeling of grass or pebbles on their knees. When they bear walk up a hill, they use a combination of creeping and climbing. Gaining in independence, nine-month-old babies cover longer distances, exploring more places in their environment.

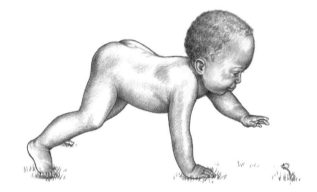

Adult Movement Explorations

Important note: please check to make sure this exploration is suitable for you. If you have specific problems—hiatal hernia, high blood pressure, retinal, heart, or neck problems—or if you are pregnant or are menstruating, don't explore this movement.

164

In the following movement explorations, your knees are flexed and your elbows are flexing and extending.

Bear Standing and Bear Walking

- Begin in the hands-and-knees position.
- Bring one foot after the other into the standing position.
- Push through your hands, extending your arms but keeping your elbows soft, and your knees flexed with your feet positioned under your hips.

- The act of pushing deeply into the ground with your hands lengthens your back, shoulders, and legs.
- Notice the position of your spine in relationship to the ground.

- Look at each hand as you reach forward; bear walk (cross-lateral movement) around the room, outside on the grass, or up a hill.
- Return to the hands-and-knees position, then to heel sitting to rest, or…

- Lie on your back with your knees flexed and your feet in contact with the floor.

The benefits of this exercise
- *lengthens the spine*
- *increases flexibility in the joints*
- *stimulates deep breathing*
- *provides the organs with a wonderful internal massage*

165

I have used this exercise successfully with all ages from children to seniors. Many people, young or old, may discover they have stiff ankles and tight hamstrings. If your hamstrings are tight, the movement may occur in your spine instead of your hips. If you find this movement difficult even with your knees flexed, choose a wide enough staircase and climb up the stairs on your hands and your feet. This movement exploration should not cause any discomfort or pain. Move within your comfort range and ability. Remember that your aim is to move with grace and ease while gaining strength, flexibility, and refined coordination.

Sitting

Remember how your seven-month-old could only reach independent sitting from her hands and knees? During that month, she began to use a more stable ring-sitting position while playing with a toy. By now, she has probably also achieved long sitting, with legs extended, or a combination of both ring sitting and long sitting, with one leg flexed and the other leg extended. This month, your baby may add W-sitting to her repertoire. In this position, a baby moves from hands and knees to sitting, positioning her pelvis between her legs. This isn't an ideal sitting position because the pelvis remains too stable, so that babies have difficulty moving out of it. Her experimentation this month leads your baby to side sitting, a more dynamic position that increases her opportunities to transition back onto hands and knees to creep and explore her environment.

James rotates his right foreleg under him to move onto his hands and knees.

Sitting has become a functional position for your baby. Her world is literally at her fingertips this month: she practices her fine motor skills by zooming in on small objects, picking them up, transferring them from hand to hand, and rotating her forearm to drop them. Some babies may be more active than others, but most babies at this age will combine their gross and fine motor skills during their play explorations.

Have you ever wondered how and when your baby learns to distinguish the weight of an object? Let's go over what

166

we have learned so far about the baby's handling skills. In the prone position, at four months, babies can distinguish between handling a soft plushy toy and scratching a textured carpet. We noticed that Mara shaped her thumb and index finger so she could clasp the desired yellow link. At six months, babies in the prone position can bang and wave toys around and can pass them from hand to hand. Independent sitting is a significant event that frees the baby's arms and hands for new play explorations and learning. Around eight months, babies develop the ability to increase their hand pressure to maintain a firm grip and to decrease their pressure to release toys. Babies can hold on to a toy and rotate (supinate/pronate) their forearm to see all sides of the toy, which provides them with a three-dimensional understanding of objects. This brief overview of handling skills and independent sitting shows that it is important for babies to have improved hand dexterity and the ability to maintain a firm grip before they can skillfully handle and manipulate heavier toys and objects. Therefore, provide your baby with age-appropriate toys to facilitate her developing manual skills.

Sense of Timing

Your baby's sense of timing is more apparent this month in her vocalizing, body movement, and rhythmic coordination. Hands-and-knees creeping is your baby's primary locomotion pattern, and she continues to refine her coordination by speeding up the pace and changing directions. As she accelerates her creeping, your baby may slap her hands on the floor, making rhythmic, staccato sounds. Babies learn to vary their pace and timing by practicing their movement skills over and over again. In her book, *Moving and Knowing*, Lydia Gerhardt also describes the baby's physical time, "The rhythm and synchronization of his body movement reflects the child's sense of time. He builds a rhythmic flow into his walking, running, or crawling. ...As the child's movement rhythm carries him through time it also moves him through space."

167

Rhythmic Dialogues: Peer Play

In the following two vignettes, you will learn how three babies use their sense of rhythm and timing to interact with each other. All three babies are close in age and can creep on hands and knees. They all use a variety of sitting postures: ring sitting, long sitting, side sitting, and W-sitting.

In play, babies at this age practice both their gross and fine motor skills. Once babies clap their hands together to show their pleasure, the game of pat-a-cake can be introduced. Although you may think of it as only a rhyming game, playing pat-a-cake with your baby reinforces her action of bringing her hands together at the midline of her body. She also gains a better understanding of how word-sounds emphasize action rhythms. Tactile input to hands, midline development, rhythmic sounds, and social interaction all come together in this little fun game. In social interaction, babies continue to illustrate how they use actions to communicate before words.

Nine-month-old babies can now keep a firm grip of a toy or object. In the first vignette, two babies illustrate how this ability facilitates their play and their success in social interaction.

Tapping Cups Vignette.

Tapping Cups Vignette

Mara holds a red stacking cup; James is sitting nearby and he grasps a green cup. He turns around and, illustrating his precise motor control, taps his cup on Mara's cup, making rhythmic sounds. Both babies enjoy this action and the rhythmic sounds they make. Their delight in playing this game is readily seen in their smiling faces and repetition of the interaction.

The differences in skill level of nine-month-old babies may be seen in their sense of timing. In the second vignette, three babies have their eye on a soft, plushy toy, but one baby seizes the opportunity to capture the desired toy first.

Ladybug, Ladybug: Peer Trio Vignette

All three babies have their eyes focused on a little wicker basket that contains a colorful ladybug. Mara sees James open the top of the basket, revealing the ladybug. With exquisite precision, Mara maneuvers her hand into the basket to get the ladybug before the top closes. Her anticipation, agility, and smooth coordination come into play when the environment offers an opportunity for action. Each baby takes turns vocalizing and waving the ladybug about. Gabrielle shakes the ladybug vigorously, James squeezes the ladybug, and Mara makes buzzing sounds along with smooth flying movements, mimicking her mother's actions with the ladybug used when they play together. Gabrielle picks up a little ribbon. Mara eyes the ribbon and tries to offer Gabrielle the soft toy. Gabrielle is still exploring what she can do with the ribbon. Gabrielle is more interested in Mara and moves toward her to touch her foot and her face. Mara shows her delight at this contact and claps her hands.

Pincer Grasp, Pinching, and Pointing

You may recall from the last chapter that eight-month-old babies developed lateral pinching by pressing their thumb against the side of their curled index finger to pick up small objects. At nine months, your baby is developing a new type of *pincer grasp* by pressing the pad at the end of the thumb against the index finger. During the next few months, your baby will continue to refine her pincer grasp so she can pick up small pellet-sized objects easily between the pads at the end of her thumb and index finger and transfer small objects from hand to hand using a pincer-to-pincer grasp. This more mature grasp is necessary for developing future functional skills: holding a crayon, a pencil, or a pen; and using scissors.

Your baby's pinching actions also show her ability to increase pressure between the tips of the thumb and index finger. Having learned to differentiate her index finger,

169

your baby uses it to push, poke, and point. In the case of pointing or placing the index finger on a toy or object, the opposite action occurs as the thumb separates from the index finger in an isolated gesture. The act of pointing shows the intricate connection between the baby's vision and the index finger.

The Gesture of Pointing

In *Thought Without Language*, George Butterworth and Lesley Grover state, "Manual pointing, the use of outstretched arm and index finger to denote an object in visual space, is species-specific to humans. The specialized use of the index finger can be distinguished from whole body orienting which is observed in other species."
In pointing, the thumb is differentiated from the index finger and "…can be understood as the *inverse* of the index-finger–thumb opposition involved in taking a precise grip; i.e. pointing involves activating the opposite movement pattern to the pincer grip and hence is not a simple extension of grasping."

A surprising amount of research has been done on the relationship of the mother and baby to understand the meaning of the "pointing gesture." In peer play, nine-month-old babies incorporate pointing into their body language and their expressive dialogues with each other. Pointing is not only a functional skill but also an expressive communication skill. When your baby points to something, you can follow the direction of his index finger to the object or toy that interests him. Babies begin to achieve more precision in communicating by pointing at what they want.

We have already seen a full range of gestures, postures, and vocalizations that eight-and nine-month-old babies use to communicate a variety of intentions. Now these babies begin to consistently use several nonverbal behaviors that specifically communicate their intent. Let's see how this plays out in the following vignette between Gabrielle and James who are sitting on a blanket outside. James has already illustrated his precise motor control by tapping Mara's cup.

170

Pointing Vignette

James picks up a branch that had fallen to the ground. Gabrielle grasps the other end and they both maintain a firm grip as they tug and pull the branch. The branch slides through James' hand and he ends up with the leaves in his hand. Refining his pincer grasp, he transfers one leaf from hand to hand. Gabrielle points to James' hand, indicating that she wants what he is holding. James shows that he understands this communication by dropping the leaf, and Gabrielle picks it up.

Pointing Vignette.

Holding an Object with the Index Finger

Butterworth and Grover note, "The infant of 8 or 9 months who is particularly interested in an object will simultaneously touch it with the index finger, while closely observing the exploration." In peer play, babies also communicate what they want to hold on to, as a precursor of ownership; for example, one baby places her index finger on a toy or object to hold it. When both babies focus on the same object, both actions come into play—pointing and then placing the index finger on the desired toy or object. Before they learn to use words, babies use gestures to communicate and to implement the action plans they have created to get what they want.

Points with index finger.

Lateral pinch.

171

Blue Ball Vignette.

Blue Ball Vignette

Both babies want the larger blue ball and James reaches for it. However, Gabrielle is holding a small red ball in one hand, and places her other index finger on the blue ball, holding the ball with this contact. James still has his eyes on the desired blue ball and develops an action plan to get it. He picks up a small orange ball and skillfully throws the ball overhand with strategic preciseness so that it lands right beside the blue ball. Visually matching the similar color and size to the red ball she is holding, Gabrielle reaches for the orange ball, releasing her contact of the blue ball. James then reaches and gets the blue ball.

The significance of these vignettes between two nine-month-old babies is that James is simultaneously aware of the leaf he is playing with and aware of Gabrielle's attention to what he is doing. In the same way, when Gabrielle places her finger on the blue ball, she is also fully aware of James' desire to get the ball, even though she is not looking at him. In these two vignettes, the babies are expanding their field of attention to include both their own activities and the other baby's focus of attention. By following the story vignettes each month, you have learned how you can more accurately determine your baby's intention by closely observing what her actions mean as they become deliberate action sequences.

172

In Your Journal

Back care has been an integral part of your ongoing movement explorations, and you will now accumulate the benefits of all your previous movement explorations. Even though your baby is getting heavier, you will notice that you carry her with ease while maintaining a dynamic body alignment in all positions – from lifting to standing.

Listen to your body. There will be days when you want to just rest. Your breathing and vocalizing explorations can be recuperative after a sleepless night. Write down your experiences for this month, reflecting on what changes in yourself you have become aware of since beginning these explorations.

Does your baby use a variety of sitting positions while playing? Can you identify and name them? How does understanding your baby's handling explorations and fine motor development help you tune in to her body language?

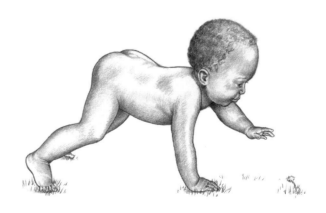

Nine-Month Highlights

Movement Development and Learning
- Side sitting, W-sitting
- Cruising
- Handling Explorations and Skills
  - Hands used for separate functions
  - Maintains a firm grip
  - Releases objects into containers
  - Perceives weight
  - Throws a ball overhand
  - Points with index finger
  - Picks up small objects

Locomotion
- Cross-Lateral Patterns
  - Creeping on hands and knees
  - Bear walking
  - Climbing

Spatial Awareness
- Changes levels
  - Supported standing and squatting

Communication and Social Interactions
- Postures and gestures
- Babbling
- Pointing
- Claps hands

Baby-Parent
  - Ball play

Peer play
  - Possession of object with index finger
  - Mimics rhythms
  - Looks, touches, gestures, and vocalizes

174

Connecting Feelings and Thoughts in Action

Ten Months

Your active explorer is climbing up and over everything in his path. In their mobile play explorations this month, babies use a wide variety of sitting positions they can transition in and out of easily. Dynamic play explorations and social interactions offer your ten-month-old many opportunities to link actions, movement patterns, and babbling into longer sequences. Even when your baby is sitting quietly inspecting a toy, you will find him practicing a variety of ways to hold, handle, and release the toy. For this reason, he will particularly enjoy container play this month, dropping things into containers and taking them out.

A budding scientist, he is busy experimenting in his environment and making new connections and discoveries that are the physical foundation of many future cognitive concepts. For example, he can now recognize, when he drops a toy from his high chair, that it takes longer before he hears the sound of the toy hitting the floor than the time it takes when he drops a toy into a wastepaper basket. This is one of the many

We now know what has always seemed intuitively true—that separating the mind from the body or nature from nurture—is impossible. Every biological process leaves a psychological imprint, and every psychological event changes the architecture of the brain.

—Thomas R. Verny,
Tomorrow's Baby: The Art and Science of Parenting

175

actions your baby performs every day that lead to his understanding the concept of "time through space."

Through actively listening to all the sounds and voices surrounding him for many months, your baby has now become a delightful communicator, ready to engage in new vocal games. He may like babbling for the sheer sensory stimulation of lips smacking, tongue clicking, and vocalizing a string of vowels and consonants together. He may move his hands along with this vocal display, adding rhythmic gestures to each vocal message.

Movement Organizes Emotions

By ten months, your baby will have a vast repertoire of expressive movements that he uses in a variety of social and play interactions. When distressed, he might act out a whole story! His body movement is the outward expression that tells us what he is feeling.

In the following vignette, you will learn how James' full-movement repertoire comes into play. All the other babies in the group are playing with several yellow balls that fit easily in their hands. James wants a yellow ball too. Assessing the situation, James' mother gathers up several balls and begins juggling. However, James doesn't want to be entertained or distracted. James responds by moving his body in a dynamic spiraling motion. He changes his body position and spatial levels to face different directions, linking several movement patterns together. Even a simple game between peers can turn into an emotional workout for a parent as she tries to decide the best course of action. When babies get frustrated they can physically disrupt a play session. In this situation, although visibly distressed, James doesn't need to be soothed, nor does he fall to pieces; instead, he responds in a robust way, revealing his strong sense of self-organization.

Now let's look in more detail at how James communicates what he is experiencing and how he handles the situation before he is ready to play again.

Story in Action Vignette

From the sitting position, James leans forward, crosses the midline of his body, slaps the floor with both hands, and immediately returns to sitting. Then he turns his body a quarter turn and spirals onto his hands and knees and changes body levels to end up in the prone position. He pushes forward with his hands and his body moves backward. He spirals upward and changes spatial levels to return to the sitting position. Now he is sitting in the same position and facing the same direction he began, that is, facing his mother. Regaining his composure, he is ready to interact once more.

What is James telling us? Because his gestures alone aren't adequate to express his deeper feelings and needs, his whole body movement repertoire automatically comes into play. The sheer quantity of tactile, vestibular, kinesthetic, and visual stimulation that James receives through his actions, helps him sort out what he is feeling in this situation. James has all the patterns of movement organization available to him through his previous experience, so that once he starts this spiraling dance, these patterns are automatically coordinated and linked together into a fluid sequence.

Babies with an extensive "movement vocabulary" are able to communicate their feelings or needs effectively, even in this preverbal stage. James can't yet say what he is upset about, but through his body language, his message is clear: he doesn't want to be distracted or entertained! He simply wants a ball to play with, and he is not happy to just watch his mother's juggling game. James doesn't just sit and cry; he modulates his intense feelings and communicates how strongly he feels through his repertoire of active movements. When James returns to the sitting position, he has regained his composure and he is ready to interact again.

Dance of Development

In this spiraling dance, a ten-month-old baby organizes his emotions. His whole body movement repertoire automatically comes into play.

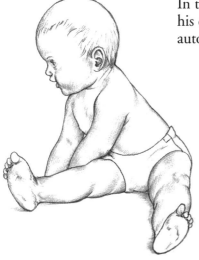

1 Reaches across the midline of the body to slap the floor.

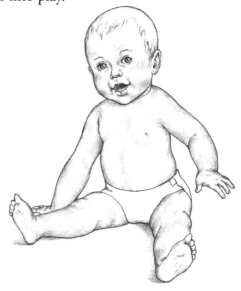

2 Protective extension to the side.

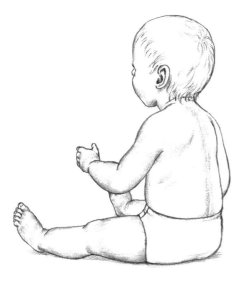

7 Arrives facing the same direction he started.

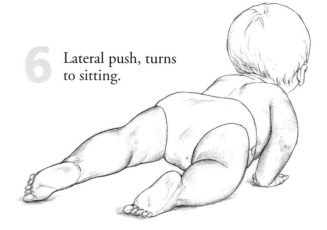

6 Lateral push, turns to sitting.

3 Turns and rolls onto hands and knees.

4 Arrives on hands and knees.

5 Symmetrical push, slides backward.

Adult Movement Explorations

Linking Movement Patterns

The following exploration links all the developmental movement sequences together that your baby has been practicing.

- Prepare on a smooth or carpeted floor, not ceramic tile.
- Sit in the ring position with your hands resting lightly on the floor at your sides.
- Turn your head to the right and shift your weight on to your right hip.
- Reach with your left hand across your midline and continue turning onto hands and knees.
- You are now facing a new direction.
- While maintaining your organ support, push with both hands so that both your legs slide out behind you until they are fully extended.
- Notice as you are pushing, you are supported on both hands with extended elbows.
- Lower your body to the floor, flexing your arms to support yourself on your forearms (symmetrical position).
- Look to the right side and as your tailbone laterally curves to the right, release your right leg to flex and bring your right hand closer to your right knee (lateral position).
- Keep looking to the right so that you move to a higher level (spinal reach).
- Continue pivoting your body around to the ring sitting position.
- Notice that you are facing the same direction you began.

Practice so that you can transition smoothly as you change spatial levels.

180

Climbing Up

Your baby continues to explore climbing up, and in a variety of new situations, she adds climbing down. In climbing, babies use the same cross-lateral movement pattern as in hands-and-knees creeping, but instead of being horizontal to the ground they are now climbing in a diagonal relationship to the ground. Climbing up a few steps or up and over objects is a favorite activity for most babies at this stage. In climbing up steps, your baby is actively exploring her surroundings. As she climbs higher, she is expanding her concept of space both above and below her.

Climbing Down

Last month, your nine-month-old baby may have explored climbing up a few steps but he probably wasn't able to climb down. This month, he will still need supervision as he tackles climbing up steps. Although he will look behind before moving backward to climb down, he needs you close by for safety.

When your baby is sliding off a sofa, a bed, or your lap, and with his first attempts at climbing backward down steps, you will notice him reaching with both feet together to move to a lower level. Initiating the movement by reaching into space with both feet together is a new symmetrical movement pattern. At eleven months you will notice him reaching out with both hands together to grasp a ball rolling by.

Reaching with both feet together.

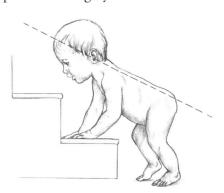

Head-to-tail organization in a diagonal relationship to the ground.

Vocalizing

The sounds your baby makes are becoming clearer as she strings vowels and consonants together. The quantity and quality of babbling in some babies becomes apparent in a stream of mouth-stimulating activities that can run nonstop at this stage. She may finely coordinate her vocalizing with expressive opening and closing movements of her hands. Babies are influenced by their surroundings, so your baby might lead a call and response game with another parent in your parent-baby group. The tuned-in parent across the room may recognize your baby's vocal game and respond, continuing a cycle of reciprocal communication. Researchers have documented that the preverbal vocalizations of parents and babies display rhythms and timing very similar to those in an adult dialogue.

I have often used the following vocal explorations with adults in my breathing and voice sessions to help them shape their lips and tongues to articulate sounds more clearly and make them more aware of their mouths in the physical aspects of speech. You may find that you can't trill your tongue or vibrate your lips as easily as you thought. You may even feel a little self-conscious and laugh a lot when you begin. You might want to begin with a humming sound, *Mmm, mmm, mmm.* Make the sound from your lips, not your throat. Sense the feeling between your lips. Observe your baby's vocalizations, and you will soon learn! This is a wonderful, playful exercise to do when your baby is watching and listening to you. You can vocalize and laugh together as she responds with her own delightful sounds.

Mara vocalizes and leads a call and response game with hand gestures.

Parent-Baby Vocal Interactions

Call and Response Game

When your baby makes a sound and looks at you from across a room

- Vocalize *ah* back to your baby, and pause.

- Wait to see if she mimics your call.
- Notice if she changes the rhythm, for instance, calling *ah-ah*.
- You might add *ah-ah* or elongate and make a sighing sound *aaahhh* and end the cycle of communication.

You will recognize when your baby is no longer interested and wants a change of pace.

Adult Vocal Explorations

These explorations stimulate and relieve tension in and around the mouth, jaw, and neck.

Liven Your Lips

Kissing Fish Make soft lip pops by bringing lips together and quickly opening your mouth.

Trucks Go Bbrr We have all heard toddlers making truck sounds like *bbrr-r-r*. Babies also make these sounds. Feel the effervescent stimulation of your lips. Explore the sounds softly and then project the sounds a little more.

Wake Up Your Tongue

Tongue Trills With your mouth open, curl your tongue upwards and make long trilling sounds with your tongue.

Clicking and Clucking Curl your tongue to make clicks and clucking sounds.

If your baby isn't making these sounds yet, you will encourage her as she watches and listens to you.

The call and response game works best when you join in after you notice your baby making sounds. Remember not to get too exuberant and take over the game. Sometimes you may just want to be attentive to the different sounds your baby makes from singsong vocalizing to high-pitched squeals. Other times, because you are tuned in to her body language, you will know whether she wants you to interact in her vocal game.

Handling Similar Toys and Objects

Your baby's body movement development and his visual and tactile explorations are the underlying components necessary for his new fine motor skills. For instance, your baby now recognizes two similar objects, like a drumstick and a musical recorder. When the objects are the right size, he can grasp and hold two objects in one hand and transfer them from hand to hand and hand to mouth. Let's take a closer look at how Colm performs these actions.

Drumstick and Recorder Vignette.

Drumstick and Recorder Vignette

Colm picks up a drumstick with one hand and transfers it to his other hand. He picks up a recorder and also transfers it to the other hand, and he now holds both objects in the same hand. With an underhand grip, he grasps the recorder and illustrates his exquisite timing and fine dexterity by doing two actions simultaneously. Colm taps the drumstick on the recorder while manipulating the correct end to his mouth. Then, he blows into the recorder, making a whistling sound.

Notice this key development that Colm uses each hand separately to perform a different action. You will see this bimanual ability more frequently as your baby develops. When he reaches the toddler stage and he is playing with a windup toy, he will be able to use one hand to hold on to the toy and use the other hand to wind the knob. With improving control, he will hold on to a piece of paper with one hand and cut the paper with play scissors that he holds in the other hand. We often forget the complexity and subtle eye-hand coordination needed to achieve this level of dexterity in his fine motor skills. All these differing functions that we take for granted are based on your baby's early developing bimanual abilities. Now we can more readily appreciate Colm's sophisticated handling skills that enable him to create and carry out this action plan. His practice in play promotes his refined handling abilities and provides him with the pleasurable feeling of self-mastery.

Container Play

When your baby is sitting and first begins dropping toys in empty containers, he may use the rim of the container for hand support. After gaining some experience in rotating his forearm, your ten-month-old baby can easily drop the object into a large container. He is developing the concept of *in* and *out* while engaging in container play. At the same time, he is actively listening to the sound that the toy or object makes when it hits the bottom.

Active focus and active listening are key in his understanding his experiment. From the moment of release, there is a pause before the toy or object hits the bottom of the container. This pause will be shorter or longer, depending on how high he holds the toy. Timing the release of the object and anticipating the sound are the elements that make this game so interesting to a baby, which is why he plays it over and over again, dropping toys from various heights.

The pause between the action and the sound the toy makes is similar to the pause between the baby's vocalized sound and the adult's vocalized response. There is now a dawning awareness of the "silent space" between sounds. This awareness is a profound development, and parents and adults who don't wait for a baby to respond in dialogue tend to "talk at" their baby. It's important to "talk with" your baby, engaging him as a participant in order to reinforce his communication abilities. If you let him take the lead in your play together, you let him know that you enjoy his unique way of communicating.

Pincer Grasp and Pinching

Last month we focused on your baby's development of his pincer grasp. Ten-month-old babies use a more mature pincer grasp and practice developing this skill using a pincer-to-pincer transfer of objects between their hands. At ten months, babies increase pressure using a pinching action. Don't assume that this pinching is an aggressive action, even if he pinches the nose of a soft toy bear. If you say "No, no!" or remove his hand, the message your baby

Timing the release of an object and anticipating the sound.

185

Pinching the bear's nose and pointing to the tail of the bear.

receives is "That is not appropriate behavior." If, instead, you model the behavior of stroking the stuffed bear and saying "Nice," but your baby continues to pinch the bear, you might recognize that he is not interested in using his whole hand in the act of stroking, but instead wants to practice his pincer and pinching grasps. As described throughout Chapter 8, your baby has been learning how to increase and decrease pressure. Pinching is a tactile experience necessary for refining the development of his fine motor skills. When you recognize that the act of pinching is the precursor of future functional skills, such as holding a crayon or using scissors, this information might help you to view your baby's pinching actions in a different light.

A creative and supportive alternative would be to provide your baby with appropriate materials to pinch, such as brightly colored playdough. The baby and parent could both make designs by pinching and poking the playdough. By reinforcing your baby's functional skills, you reinforce his expressive social interactions and build his self-esteem.

Hiding Games

Catherine Garvey, writing about infants and play, informs us that, "What strikes him as amusing now appears to involve not only sound or motion as such but some contrast between expectation and perception." In your natural understanding of this, as a parent, you probably introduced your baby to the game of peekaboo some months ago, hiding your face behind your hands or placing a blanket over a doll. Engaging her in your game of peekaboo, your baby shows her delight by squealing with glee at the element of surprise built into this game.

Now, you may have noticed that your baby wants to lead her own game of peekaboo. Garvey, in *Play*, goes on to say, "…just as a child becomes more active in creating the conditions for a humor response, so does he become more active in play—moving, for example, from an audience role in peekaboo to an active role by covering his own or his mother's face." In the following vignette, Mara initiates the game by hiding her face with a beach

186

ball and engages James and his mother as the audience in her game of peekaboo.

> ### Peekaboo Vignette
>
> *Mara initiates a game of peekaboo with James and his mother. Playing with a colorful beach ball, she uses this ball to hide her face. Holding the ball between her hands, she peeks out from the left side and then from the right side. When Mara raises the beach ball in front of her face she "disappears." Peeking from the left side, she "appears"; in the center, she "disappears"; peeking from the right side, she "reappears."*

What does this vignette tell us about Mara's play? For one thing, she is using a ball as an object to cover and hide her face. She is not using it to play a throw and catch game, which she knows. Mara uses the ball in a new way, thereby creating her game of peekaboo.

A game like this may simply be viewed by adults as funny or cute, without their examining the underlying accomplishments of the child that make her game possible. Let's take a closer look at her actions. First there is her ability to maintain a grasp of the ball while reaching across her midline without losing her balance. Then she clearly illustrates her intent that it is not just by chance that she performs the action of reaching across her midline with the ball, because she repeats the action to the other side while also still holding on to the ball. Third, she is able to regulate her excitement as she coordinates both her physical actions and social interactions at the same time. She wants James and his mother to watch and participate in her humorous game.

Although at first sight this may look like a game of "imitation," and that Mara is merely re-creating an action that she has seen someone else perform, we can't assume that Mara has seen a ball used in this way. However, even if this is the case, Garvey points out that, "imitation itself is a gradually emerging achievement that rests on both

Peekaboo Vignette.

187

mental and physical development." She continues, "At this time a child does not have verbal labels for action sequences or for objects, and his 'concept' of an object is based on the sensory feedback of his experience with it." Based on these accomplishments, we must marvel at a young baby's ability to take the lead in an interactive game that demonstrates her competency to develop a preverbal game plan, her engaging social skills, and her budding sense of humor.

James Gets the Joke Vignette

Sitting with his back to Mara, James is facing his mother and playing a ball game. He picks up a colorful striped beach ball, lifts it up, and momentarily holds it on top of his head. Mara, who is sitting behind him, suddenly sees this beautiful ball coming over his head toward her, and she is ready to get it. She grasps it from James' hands. In a split second, he gets the gist of the interaction. Without turning around, James figures out the ball play and knowingly smiles.

This vignette of social interaction in spontaneous ball play provides a humorous exchange between two babies. The episode also contains the feature of something disappearing, literally behind James' back. It is the element of surprise and James' recognition of what has occurred that makes it funny.

In his book, *The Interpersonal World of the Infant,* Daniel Stern tells us that, "…soon after nine months of age, the beginning of jokes and teasing on the infant's part can be seen." He adds, "You can't tease other people unless you can correctly guess what is 'in their minds' and make them suffer or laugh because of your knowing." Mara is teasing James by interrupting his game plan for playing with the ball.

James Gets the Joke Vignette.

188

In Your Journal

Notice that you have been combining more movements together in the last two months. Are your movements more effortless? Do you hold your breath at any point, or do you breathe easily throughout your movement explorations?

How have your movement and vocal explorations enhanced your social interactions with your baby? These explorations not only refine your awareness, but help you become more sensitive to your baby's subtle communication cues.

Write down the actions that your baby likes to do. Share with others who take care of your baby your understanding of what has been important this month in your baby's actions, social interactions, and learning. Take some time from your busy schedule to take a few photos as special reminders of your FloorPlay time together.

Ten-Month Highlights

Movement Development and Learning

- Ring, long, side, and W-sitting
- Protective extension backward
- Supported standing, squatting, cruising
- Handling Explorations and Skills
    - Hands used for separate functions
    - Releases objects in containers
    - Points with index finger
    - Pokes objects with index finger

- Symmetrical Patterns
    - Reaching with both feet to climb down

Locomotion

- Cross-Lateral Patterns
    - Creeping on hands and knees in a quicker rhythm
    - Climbing upstairs

Spatial Awareness

- Changes levels
    - Supported standing, squatting
    - Cruising

Communication and Social Interactions

- Postures and gestures
- Babbling, lip and tongue sounds

Baby-Parent

- Call and response game
- Ball play
- Peekaboo, pat-a-cake

Peer play

- Touches, gestures, sounds
- Teases and plays a joke

Orienting in Space on Two Feet

Eleven Months

Eleven-month-old babies are capable of squatting, independent standing, and walking forward while holding on to a piece of furniture with one hand. What an exhilarating experience when your baby suddenly finds herself standing up on her own, which might occur when she is engrossed in playing with a toy. She may be so intrigued that she wants to manipulate the toy with both hands and removes her supporting hand from the furniture. Suddenly, she is standing on her own! This is a major milestone. In standing upright, the perspective of her world changes dramatically. She notices that many things that were above her are now in front of her. This month she will practice transitioning in and out of a variety of positions to come to standing. From this higher level, not only does she have to organize her body in a new relationship to gravity, but she also has to learn to get back down without holding on.

In our adult world, our awareness of *up* and *down* is so clear that we no longer perceive how we developed these concepts, based as they are on our early physical experiences. Interacting with the force of gravity is a

[The young child] … remembers the space of time and the time of space of his previous movement experiences. Memory elicits direction in thought. The thinker moves to fill the gaps between previous evidence and present perception. His thought connects points in time and space.

— Lydia Gerhardt,
Moving and Knowing

191

constant challenge in your baby's explorations of standing up and squatting down. Standing requires her to integrate all her body's movements, sensations, and interactions with gravity just to balance on two feet. The changes of level from creeping, to standing, to taking first steps, offers your baby a new scope for moving upward, facing forward, and moving outward into the world.

Spinal Curves: From C-Curve to S-Curve

You learned about your baby's developing cervical curve in the pre-locomotion stage. Have you thought about how the lumbar curve develops? In the following activities, we will broaden our understanding of how this occurs.

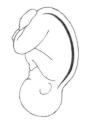

C-curve.

In the womb, the baby's spine is in a primary C-curve shape. At birth, babies begin lifting their heads to interact with the ever-present force of gravity, and by four months the first reversed curve of the spine is visible in the neck curve (cervical curve). Continuing to move against the resistance of gravity, babies progress to verticality first in independent sitting, then in independent standing and walking. All the actions that lead to these achievements shape the second reverse curve in the lumbar region of the spine (lower back) that appears when the toddler begins to walk between 12 and 18 months. In his book, *The Body Moveable*, David Gorman writes, "Its development is necessary to bring the center of gravity over the legs. It has straightened out from being concave forwards by then and by 3 years is becoming convex forwards…"

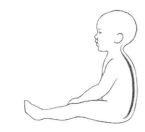

Cervical curve.

This developmental process helps us to understand how function (body movement) influences form (the spine) in the S-curve of the spine and how form provides for function. The S-shaped curves of the spine combine the qualities of strength and stability necessary for a firm supportive skeletal structure. These curves provide maximum flexibility in bending, leaning, and rotating our body and also in the spine's shock-absorbing ability for walking, running, and jumping.

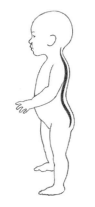

S-curve.

Spinal Organization: Head-to-Tail

The head-to-tail organization of the spine is aligned with the body's vertical axis. Regardless of one's position in space, there is always this dynamic head-to-tail organization. In the locomotion stage this can be seen in the baby's diversity of actions in space. A few of these actions are illustrated here:

Regardless of one's position in space, there is always this head-to-tail organization.

Horizontal relationship to ground.

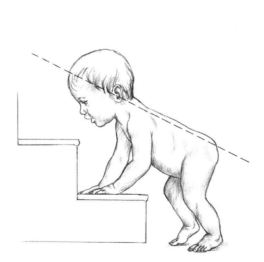

Diagonal.

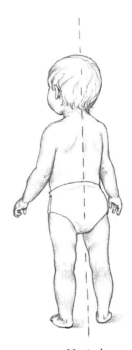

Vertical.

Moving Upward

There is no reason to rush your baby to attain early standing. When babies coordinate their bodies to balance in standing, their dynamic physical interactions with gravity ensure that they build new body-brain connections through their own experiences. Only in this way can babies embody the upright spinal head-to-tail connection. Although you may want to lift your baby up and place her in the standing position, let her pull herself up on her own. She will feel that she has grown so tall when she comes from the ground up to standing by herself. In this way, she will gain body-confidence, orient to where she is in space, be well grounded on two feet, and be ready to take her first steps in independent walking.

Midline Movement

Intimately related to the body is the concept of *laterality*, our internal sense of the two sides of our body. Leaders in the fields of body movement and sensory integration maintain that laterality must be learned by exploring body movement. Through unilateral movement patterns, a baby makes the necessary connections to learn how the two sides of his body function together. Then he learns through cross-lateral movements how the two sides of his body interact in a diagonal relationship to each other.

So how do these concepts relate to your baby? Let's review how he develops his body awareness and body image. When your baby was five or six months old, he would lie on his back, holding his feet. Maybe you noticed him holding one foot with two hands, crossing the midline of his body. In the symmetrical push patterns, your six-month-old baby learned how to distinguish his upper body from his lower body. Around seven months, your baby differentiated both halves of his body and explored how they coordinate together in belly crawling. At eight months, he added cross-lateral creeping to his developmental movement repertoire. In the cross-lateral creeping pattern, your baby crosses the midline of his body when he reaches with one hand to shift his weight forward and pulls his opposite leg forward. Hands-and-knees creeping, by involving movements that cross the midline of the body through this diagonal pattern, integrates both sides of the brain. When your baby begins walking, it will be several months before you notice that he can walk in a cross-lateral pattern.

Your child's ability to focus on activities that require cross-lateral movement across the midline of his body is a key development: it means that he is no longer limited to using one hand to perform activities on one side of his body and the other hand to perform activities on the other side of his body. Developing this ability is essential for your child's many future activities: coloring, using scissors, playing sports, playing a musical instrument, and developing skills in reading and writing. Integration of the two sides of his body is necessary before your child can develop his capacity to discriminate between his body's right and left sides.

Six Basic Directions

Through body movement, the child organizes her directions in space. We can describe body movement in space by using six basic directions. Assuming a beginning position of standing on two feet, these directions are

- upward – downward: changing levels along the spine's axis,
- leftward – rightward: reaching or stepping to the side,
- forward – backward: advancing or retreating, as in creeping or walking forward or backward.

Upward – Downward

Since her eighth month, your baby has been using different stable objects to pull herself upright. She aligns her body with the furniture in her surroundings to achieve her vertical posture. In doing so, she learns what it feels like to balance in the upright position before sitting or squatting down. In the eleventh month, babies find that changing levels is a challenge and they

Mara initiates a change of direction by first moving her right foot backward and then begins creeping forward.

195

experiment with a variety of positions to move upward, to stand, and to move downward to squat on two feet.

Rightward – Leftward

At nine months, babies use both hands on stable objects they find when cruising. When a baby faces a long bench or low piece of furniture and sees a toy far to her right, she learns to reach it by walking sideways to the right. Coordinating her hands and feet to move in synchrony, she rhythmically combines her walking hands with her side-stepping feet. During her eleventh month, your baby will likely be confident enough to turn her body sideways to the furniture and walk forward using only one hand for support.

Forward – Backward

Before babies walk forward and backward through space, they creep forward and backward. This is a significant change in relationship to gravity: one has a vertical relationship and one has a horizontal relationship to the ground.

Some babies are able to walk forward as early as ten or eleven months, but other babies may not do so until they are well over a year. In new walking, your baby's posture, timing, coordination, and balance are refined over many months. A later development is the baby's ability to turn and look behind before walking backward through space, an action you see when a toddler pulls a toy across the floor.

Creeping Forward

Your baby rotates her spine to creep forward in a smoother pattern. While she is creeping on hands and knees, you might see her stop to reach for a toy, extending her opposite arm and leg. With increasing control of her body, she can perform this cross-lateral action by balancing on one hand and the opposite leg to maintain this position. See Chapter 7 for the adult cross-lateral creeping exploration.

Creeping forward with more rotation in her spine.

Reaching with the hand to creep forward.

Looking and reaching with the foot to creep backward.

Read the description of how your baby creeps backward and try it for yourself.

Creeping Backward

When your baby can't creep forward to go where she wants, she will back up. Backing up or retreating requires her to change direction. To initiate this action, she may turn around to look backward before reaching back with the foot that's on the same side she is facing, or she may just reach back a little with one foot. As she reaches backward with her foot, her opposite hand also moves backward. In some situations, small adjustments in one foot may be all that is needed to change direction and may not lead to creeping backward. Learning to creep backward facilitates your baby's ability to get in and out of tight corners or to get past something or someone blocking her way.

197

Bear standing to squatting to standing.

Standing, Squatting, and Bear Standing

Now suddenly her hands are free and she is standing alone! Standing requires your baby to integrate all her body's movements, sensations, and interactions with gravity in order to balance on two feet. For several months, she has been practicing a variety of movements that lead to independent standing: kneeling to standing, half-kneeling to standing, two-hand supported cruising, to one-hand support in forward walking. The ability to carry out these sequences will vary from baby to baby.

However, even for babies who are already walking, to move back down from standing to squatting is a challenge. The first few times, you may see her body wobble a little forward and a little backward to get there, then she loses her balance and sinks to the floor, not once but many times. Undaunted, she learns that falling is part of the dance. Squatting is the natural way that children change levels to stand up or to lower themselves back down to the floor or the ground. They are the world's best squatters.

The action of squatting may be a lost component in our adult movement repertoire, but you can learn to do this action in your own exploration this month and discover just how beneficial this movement is. Many cultures that don't depend on chairs use this position in their daily routines.

Bear Standing: A Transition

Bear standing becomes a transition position when your baby moves from hands and knees to squatting and from standing to squatting. From hands and knees, she shifts her weight forward onto her hands. She places one foot under her to support herself on her hands and one foot, and then she brings her other foot forward so that she is now bear standing.

Moving upward to independent standing is a challenge from the squat position. Ankle support and responsive feet are necessary for balance and control. Your baby pushes both feet against the floor and then extends her knees in independent standing. Once she can maintain standing, she can flex her knees and lower her body into a squat position. When a baby squats, her heels maintain contact with the ground to develop ankle stability. Attracted by a toy, babies often play for a long time in the squatting position. From squatting, your baby can easily transition to hands and knees and resume creeping.

Adult Movement Explorations

Diagonal Reach of Arm and Opposite Leg

Breathe easily throughout the exploration.

- Assume the hands-and-knees position.
- Look down and focus on your right hand.
- Follow the movement of your right hand with your eyes.
- Sliding your right hand and left foot in contact with the floor…

When you are reaching for a ball, notice that your head is not in a static position. Your eyes follow the movement of your hand.

Diagonal reach forward for a toy with opposite arm and leg.

199

- Simultaneously reach forward with your right hand and reach backward with your left foot, extending both your arm and leg.
- Balance on your left hand and right leg.
- Continue to look at your right hand, and return to the hands-and-knees position.
- Look down and focus on your left hand.
- Follow the movement of your left hand with your eyes.
- Sliding your left hand and right foot in contact with the floor…
- Simultaneously reach forward with your left hand and reach backward with your right foot, extending both your arm and leg.
- Balance on your right hand and left leg.
- Continue to look at your left hand, and return to the hands-and-knees position.
- Your scapulas (shoulder blades) remain down.
- Explore this diagonal action 3 times.

Squatting: Holding a Ball

Most adults have difficulty squatting and many do not have flexible enough ankle joints to maintain their whole foot on the ground as a child does. Holding a large gymnastic ball provides an outer focus and will help you to release your heels into the floor. With practice, you will improve the coordination among all your joints. Release any breath holding and breathe easily throughout the movement.

Cautionary note: this movement may be difficult for you to do for the following reasons:

- *inflexibility,*
- *movement inexperience,*
- *previous injury.*

If so, begin slowly and don't go down into a full squat. Simply go as far as is comfortable (see second photo) and rise to standing again. With experience over time, you will expand your range of motion.

Babies often hold a toy in their hand to maintain balance in the early stages of their standing and walking. In the following exercise, hold a large gymnastic ball between your hands. While holding and focusing on the ball, your arms and breathing will remain relaxed, and you will find this movement easier. Experiment by holding balls of different sizes.

- Stand with your feet shoulder-width apart.
- Hold a ball between your hands and extend your arms forward.
- Focus on the ball as you lower the ball, and flex your knees to the squat position.
- Continue to hold the ball between your hands.
- Maintain the squat position for as long as you are comfortable (your heels may be off the floor).
- Hold the ball securely between both hands and push down into the floor with your feet.
- Look at the ball between your hands as you rise to standing.
- Notice the flexibility of your knee and ankle joints.
- Explore gently, you should not at any point experience any pain.

Benefits: in the adult, the action of squatting helps lengthen stiff back muscles, widens the rib cage for deeper breathing, and increases flexibility in hip, knee, and ankle joints. In the squatting position, there is a gentle pressure of the thighs against the abdominal organs that stimulates and improves digestion.

Squat to Communicate with Your Budding Toddler

At each stage, you have been learning how to change your body position to interact body-to-body and face-to-face with your baby. Communicating at your baby's level has

provided you with a new way of relating throughout his first year. Squatting may be a challenge for you, but as you continue practicing, you will slowly improve; the action of squatting will keep you fit and at the same time expand your communication and social interactions with your budding toddler.

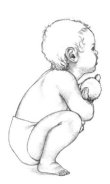

Squatting improves the flexibility of your hip, knee, and ankle joints. Your ability to lower into a squat and rise to standing in a smooth synchronized action is important for protecting your back in everyday functions, especially for lifting and lowering your baby to the floor.

Adult Movement Explorations

Creeping to Standing

In this exercise, it may help to have a small ball placed in front of you. As you move to a half-kneeling standing position, pick up the ball and continue moving upward to the standing position.

- Begin in the hands-and-knees creeping stance.
- Focus on a bright colored ball placed in front of you but within reach.
- Reach with one hand to pick up the ball as you place your right foot forward in half-kneel standing.

- In a continuous motion, shift your weight forward onto your right foot and take the ball with both hands.
- Continue rising upward until you are walking forward.

Transitions to standing

Half-kneeling.

Standing.

203

Notice the change in sitting positions.

Handling Skills

In the sitting position, eleven-month-old babies can use both hands to reach for a ball nearby. At ten months, your baby developed a new symmetrical reach pattern using both feet together when climbing downstairs, off a bed, a sofa, or an adult's lap.

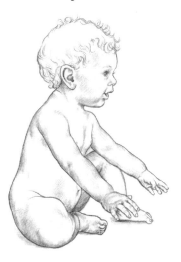

This month she probably still uses this symmetrical pattern to climb downstairs and now, in sitting, she also reaches with both hands to grasp a rolling ball. In your parent-baby group, you may notice one baby holding a ball in each hand and when she sees another ball roll by, she drops them to reach for the new ball. The other babies or their parents may get upset because she now has all three balls. However, this is a baby's natural reaching response. Remember that the action of grasping and releasing toys is still a relatively new skill and so is this baby's new movement pattern of reaching with both hands. Until now, maybe nobody noticed her new reaching pattern and yet she is just thrilled to keep trying it out!

At eight to ten months, you may notice that your baby wants a toy her friend is playing with and tries to exchange toys with her. Although babies can release toys at this age, they are not usually successful at performing this action during their play interactions. Therefore, it is

204

inappropriate to try to teach babies to share toys at this stage, because they are still developing their manual skills. Offering toys or objects to each other or to a parent may occur, but this action is more frequently seen when babies begin walking independently. At that time, they might carry a toy across a room to offer to a parent, a grandparent, a caregiver, or another child.

This month, you may be looking forward to the day your baby stands up and walks on her own. But just stop and think about how challenging her physical interactions with gravity are. Notice how attentive she is to developing her new manual skills. And as if this were not enough, she adds many new problem-solving tasks to her explorations. When you reflect on all her capabilities, you will better appreciate how she is choreographing her dance of development every day.

Pincer grasp.

Pinching with more thumb rotation.

Here and There Vignette

Gabrielle is standing next to a big red ball. First she raises her left hand and points across the room to indicate "over there." Then she reaches out to point and touch the big red ball with her index finger to indicate "here." Next she uses her right index finger to point across the room again. These tactile and gestural explorations form the foundation for a baby's developing cognitive concepts of "here" and "there" before she can physically move through space to get from "here" to "there."

Here and There Vignette.

205

Walking on an uneven surface, falling is just part of the dance.

Walking

Remember that each baby is unique and develops at her own pace. Some babies are able to walk forward as early as ten or eleven months, but other babies don't walk until they are well over a year of age. When babies walk for the first time, they stand with their feet far apart, using a wide base of support. Your baby senses the subtle shifts in her weight as she balances in walking. In this action, many body systems come into play: visual, vestibular, and kinesthetic as she seeks to balance her body movement in three-dimensional space.

Walking across a room requires your baby's full attention. Crossing any uneven surface requires her full concentration to maintain postural control, but with a loss of balance, falling is just part of the dance. Without missing a beat, she will be up on her feet again, intent on walking like everyone else. For the emerging toddler, falling is simply a way of learning to master gravity in her body's new orientation to space. Holding on to a toy may provide a better sense of control and balance. She can transfer the object hand to mouth or hand to hand while walking forward.

The progressive understanding of *here and there* and *near and far* also leads to an evolving perception of space, distance, and time. The physical experience of perceiving time, space, and energy is entwined, providing your baby with the embodied foundation to form the critical cognitive concepts for understanding her surroundings and her world.

In Your Journal

Write down your initial responses to your new movement explorations. Especially notice whether you are holding your breath at any point while you are doing them. If you are not smooth in your transitions, don't worry. It takes time, so proceed slowly. Learn from your baby who is so attentive to what she is doing. She is truly demonstrating what is known as the "beginner's mind," which means taking a fresh approach to any new learning experience. You may appreciate this concept, especially if you are a first-time parent.

Begin to reflect on your year of experiential learning, and write down what it has meant to you personally.

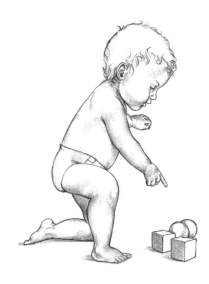

Eleven-Month Highlights

Movement Development and Learning
- Independent standing
- Independent squatting
- Supported walking
- Long sitting, side sitting
- Symmetrical Patterns
  - Reaching forward with both hands in play
  - Reaching backward with both feet to climb down
- Handling Explorations and Skills
  - Pincer grasp
  - Pinches with more thumb rotation

Locomotion
- Cross-Lateral Patterns
  - Creeping forward in a smoother rhythm
  - Creeping backward and changing direction
  - Bear walking
  - Climbing up

- Independent walking

Spatial Awareness
- Changes levels
- Changes directions

Communication and Social Interactions
- Babbling and sounds
- Pointing

Baby-Parent
  - Squatting together

Peer play
  - Postures, gestures, and babbling
  - Object play

Stepping into the World

Twelve Months

Your baby's learning experiences during the first year are astonishing. She knows how to coordinate her body through a variety of play experiences. She moves through space and can change spatial levels. Through her actions, she perceives and engages in her world from different points of view. In self-motivated play, she creates her own action plans and problem-solving activities to develop her self-mastery. You will be amazed at the depth and breadth of the connections she is making through her physical interactions with her environment.

Standing alone is an invigorating experience. On her own small feet, your baby takes her place in the world. The smile on her face shows the exhilaration she feels, as if to say, "Here I am!" It is an awesome moment. But then before you know it, she is down on hands and knees again chasing after a pet and squealing with delight. Creeping is still a favorite mode of travel, especially when your baby wants to move quickly or to move from a sitting position to get a toy. Using all her locomotion skills, she continues to develop her body awareness as mind and body become attuned to the environment

When the ability to verbally frame and remember concepts is only just beginning to develop, the brain must be stimulated through the senses.... Movement grows the brain. It is a vital key to neural development, especially in the areas of memory and higher cognitive function.

—Don Campbell, *The Mozart Effect® for Children*

Twelve-month-old babies creeping, standing, and walking.

through movement. Seeking novel experiences like lifting a foot to kick a ball, she challenges her balance and equilibrium responses and learns that stumbling and falling are just part of her learning experience.

As your baby catapults herself across a large room, she is learning about dynamic balance in her upright posture, how to maintain a stabilized course while accelerating and, at the same time, preparing to decelerate so she can stop at any moment. When she stops, her exhilarating experience may stimulate her to turn around to look at the distance she covered. Through these exciting explorations she is building a kinesthetic memory of how she functions while moving through the complex world of time and space.

Independent Walking

When your baby first begins to walk, you will notice that he uses a wide base of support for stability, and his hips are externally rotated throughout. You will also notice that his leg swing and steps are short, and that he contacts the floor with a flat foot. You will not see any toe-pushing yet as he walks, although in a variety of positions up to now, babies have been preparing their toes for push off in independent walking. Your baby may hold his arms close to his body in a high-guard position or outstretched if he has a goal in mind. You may also notice that he literally hurtles himself across a room, then stops just as abruptly. With practice, he develops more control of his body in motion and improves his rhythm and timing in stepping and stopping.

Although walking is natural, it is complex. New walkers generally range in age from nine months to fourteen months, and some may be even earlier or later. Whenever a baby walks across a room for the first time, it is certainly one of their most thrilling accomplishments to behold. By eighteen months, postural control is fairly well coordinated when walking, as the arms, having lowered, can now swing in a cross-lateral pattern.

Kicking a Ball

Walking around a room, your baby finds that her surroundings provide her with many novel situations to try out new actions. Gabrielle walks into a ball, and it rolls. She sees another ball and attempts to kick it. To accomplish this action, she briefly balances on one foot while she kicks the ball with the other foot. This action challenges her balance and equilibrium responses.

The following vignettes illustrate the actions of two babies who are gaining in independence. In both scenarios, these babies are already walking independently and start off toward their goal, to reach their mother's open arms. However, for differing reasons, they both stop and change direction.

Balancing on one foot to kick a ball.

Novel Toy Vignette

Gabrielle's mother is sitting on the other side of the room. Gabrielle looks across the room, smiles, and extends her arm toward her mother. She begins walking across the room to reach her mother's beckoning arms. Attracted by a new toy lying on the floor, Gabrielle stops short and changes direction. Following her own curiosity, she points to a new toy on the floor to convey her interest.

Don't feel disappointed if your baby starts off making a beeline for you and then changes her mind. You might at first feel that she chooses to move toward a colorful toy rather than toward your open arms. You may not be aware that your body language shows how you are feeling, as your smile vanishes. Instead, in this exciting display of her personal development, show how thrilled you feel that she can and does make independent choices when curious about her environment.

Until your baby gains more postural control, walking some distance in a straight line isn't easy; she may veer off her path when her attention is captured by an interesting object.

Novel Toy Vignette.

Time of Space Vignette.

Time of Space Vignette

Mara's sheer physical exuberance propels her across a large open room. She spontaneously stops, changes direction, and looks back across the room. During this pause, Mara integrates her perceptions of her exhilarating experience—how fast she traveled, how long it took, and the distance she covered. This kind of spontaneous action shapes the baby's early concepts of balance, energy, time, and space.

In *The Self Perceived,* Ulric Neisser also identifies this dynamic experience of walking across a room. He writes, "As you walk across a room, many kinds of information enable you to perceive your own movement and its trajectory. There is the kinesthetic feedback from joints and muscles, as well as detection of acceleration in the vestibular organs; there are the echoing sounds of your footsteps, and especially the systematic changes of optical structure available to your eyes."

Adult Movement Explorations

Finding Your Vertical Axis
Moving Forward-Backward

Note the changing pressure being exerted by your feet on the floor. These explorations stimulate

- *foot reflexes*
- *righting reactions*
- *equilibrium responses*

212

- Stand with both feet comfortably apart, positioned under your hips.
- Become aware of the even pressure exerted by both feet on the floor.
- Shift your weight forward, onto the front part of your foot, without lifting your *heels*.
- Return, align your vertical axis in relation to gravity.
- Shift your weight backward, onto your heels, without lifting your *toes*. Now experiment lifting heels/toes.
- Return, align your vertical axis in relation to gravity.

Moving Side to Side

- Stand with both feet comfortably apart, positioned under your hips. Become aware of the even pressure exerted by both feet on the floor.
- Shift your weight toward the right, keeping both feet in contact with the floor.
- Notice where the weight is on your right and left foot. Now experiment with one foot off the floor.
- From the right, shift your weight toward the left across your midline, and continue to the left.
- Notice where the weight is on your left and right foot, or is one foot off the floor?
- Return, align your vertical axis in relation to gravity.

Losing her balance, Gabrielle yields to gravity and uses a protective extension response to the side.

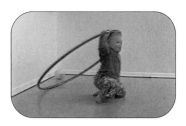

Playing outside and inside the circle of space.

Rotating around Your Vertical Axis

- Begin with your feet planted on one spot.
- Shift your weight forward; continue to shift your weight rightward, then backward, then leftward, arriving forward again, making a full circle.
- Return, align your vertical axis in relation to gravity, and pause.
- You may notice your body still moving, before your vertical axis and the force of gravity come into alignment.

Release any holding patterns, such as grasping with your toes, curling your fingers, or extending your index finger.

Before you circle to the left, compare your right foot to your left foot. Notice any differences. Compare the sides of your body.

- Circle to the left as above.

Walking: A Cross-Lateral Connection

How often do you pay attention to how you enter a new space or walk across a room? Probably not very often, at least until now. Notice any breath holding during this movement exploration.

This exercise helps to integrate both hemispheres of the brain. This movement exploration will provide you with the experience to better appreciate the next several months it takes before your baby coordinates her arms and legs to walk in a cross-lateral gait.

- Stand with your weight equally balanced on both feet.
- Focus on a point across the room.
- Prepare to step forward with your right foot.
- Lift your right heel and your knee simultaneously flexes.
- Swing phase: lift your right foot off the floor and step forward.
- Your right heel strikes the floor and your right leg extends.

- Shift your body weight forward onto your right foot. *Note: don't swing your hips side to side.*
- Move slowly and sense what happens.
- Simultaneously your left heel lifts off the floor.

Notice that your left heel lifts up off the ground as you roll onto the ball of your right foot, and your toes are ready to push off.

- Preparing for the swing phase, your left knee flexes.
- Swing phase: lift your left foot off the floor and step forward.
- Your left heel strikes the floor and your left leg extends.
- Shift your body weight forward onto your left foot. *Note: don't swing your hips side to side.*
- Move slowly and sense what happens.
- Simultaneously your right heel lifts off the floor.

Notice that your right heel lifts up off the ground as you roll onto the ball of your left foot, and your toes are ready to push off.

- Preparing for the swing phase, your right knee flexes.
- Repeat the steps slowly and mindfully as you bring your attention to your arms.
- Notice the diagonal connection between your opposite arm and leg while walking.
- Are you holding your breath or getting tense?
- Pause and gently shake your arms out, and shake each leg to free up your movement.

Many of the breathing and movement explorations you have participated in over the course of the year will remain part of your movement repertoire. Continue to explore and practice your breathing and movement explorations that by now have become integral to your daily routine—a joyful part of your life. You have probably discovered that you feel calmer, more organized, and less rushed. Each time you participate in your breathing and movement explorations, you are fine-tuning your current awareness and learning.

215

Toddlers bring objects to adults that they find interesting.

Action Plans

To set up new, complex problem-solving games, a baby needs to have an action plan in mind and be able to imagine what the outcome will be. If she meets her own expectations, she will know that she has been successful. The experience of feeling pleasure in learning follows from her evolving self-mastery.

This second half of the first year has been a dynamic stage when babies are able to move independently to explore, interact, and problem solve in their environment. They actively search out new experiences and coordinate their bodies in a variety of locomotion sequences so they can reach their goals. When babies sit independently, their arms and hands are free to develop their fine motor skills and expressive gestures.

In an environment that provides new opportunities for action, a mobile baby is quick to respond. This month we learned that the first time Gabrielle walked into a ball, she watched it roll; the next time, she lifted her foot off the ground to kick it. In their sophisticated explorations of space, babies are in nonstop mode at this stage, trying out their newfound mobility in as many ways possible.

Using EEG brain recordings, researchers have shown that the prefrontal cortex of a human baby becomes much more active between seven and twelve months. In their tests, this area "lights up," particularly during a toy-hiding exercise when a baby must hold the image of a hidden toy in her mind during a five- to ten-second delay (Diamond and Hopson, *Magic Trees of the Mind*). Let's see how this is revealed in the following vignette.

216

Remembering the Present Vignette

When walking across a room, babies are aware not only of the space in front of them but also of the space behind them. With more balance and body control, Mara can hold on to a ball with both hands and reach both arms up overhead while walking forward. She connects her action with a gesture and words into a sequence of events and remembers them.

Mara creates a more complex game that challenges her memory. Holding a ball with both hands, Mara reaches up and lets the ball fall behind her while continuing to walk forward. With a sweep of her arms, Mara says, "All gone!" For a brief time, the ball is out of sight (remember it rolled behind her) but not out of mind. Because Mara performed the sequence of actions, she knows that when she turns around, she will see the ball.

As you recall, Colm at six months sets up his own action plan. Without looking at what he is doing, Colm rolls a basket to one side of his body beyond his reach. He briefly lets go of the basket. Although it has disappeared from view, Colm knows that when he turns around, he will see the basket. In both these vignettes, there is intention in each baby's action. However, the babies do not depend on vision to set up their actions, for they sense what they are doing through touch and movement (kinesthetic receptors). They know they will be able to visually locate the object when they turn around to grasp it (the basket) or look for it (the ball), reinforcing the expected outcome of their actions.

At this age, Mara is capable of a more complex integration of action and thought; let's analyze the ball vignette in more detail. Mara picks up a yellow ball and holds it with both hands, raising the ball overhead. We observe that Mara's intention is, first of all, to drop the ball over her head so that it falls out of sight, behind her. Then we notice that she has something else in mind. How do we know this? Because when she hears the ball hit the floor and bounce, she doesn't turn around to get it. Instead, Mara continues to walk forward, gestures with both arms up in the air, and says, "All gone!" She combines her body language with her words and continues walking. She stops, then turns around, expecting to see the yellow ball behind her. Her act of locating the ball that she made disappear shows that she has integrated her kinesthetic, auditory, and visual experiences.

What meaning does this vignette have? Through her differentiated movement repertoire, Mara is able to carry out a particular succession of movements while walking across the room and remembers the sequence of events and the path she traveled. By implementing a more sophisticated plan, Mara connects her thoughts to her actions and her playful feelings of pretend. Because Mara creates the game, we know she is pretending when she says in a singsong voice that the ball is "All gone!" If she thought the ball had disappeared, she would have turned around immediately to look for it!

Mara is familiar with a variety of hiding games like peekaboo. Remember, she got James' ball when it went over his head. Mara holds the key visual image to knowing what happens in these hiding games—"what disappears, will reappear." Knowing this sequence, she can now fill in the gaps based on her present perception. In this vignette, her intention is aligned with her skillful body movements (holds the ball and releases it overhead) and her words accompany her nonverbal gesture (the upward sweep of her arms). Mara continues to walk forward for another ten steps before she says, "All gone!" which reflects her visual memory. Then she stops, turns, and faces a new direction to look behind her, knowing she will see the yellow ball. She satisfies an internal knowing that she can create her own interactions in her environment. Through her actions, Mara is forming the physical concepts of space that she will build on over the next few years. In this little vignette, the entwined body-mind interactions and embodied experiences provide us with a deep understanding of the child's mind in action.

In Your Journal

Write down what you notice in your movement explorations this month. Last month, you began to reflect on your year of experiential learning and what it has meant to you personally. Take the time to review the journal entries that you documented each month and write down some of the essential movement experiences that have made a difference to you and your relationship with your baby.

Write down what you noticed that was special in your baby's movement, social, and learning development. You have shared in a unique and fun way many hours with your baby at her level. Even though she is "graduating" to toddlerhood, she will still enjoy lots of time in FloorPlay with you. Continue to document your toddler's movement, social, and learning development as you have been doing, adding new explorations as they occur.

Twelve-Month Highlights

Movement Development and Learning
- Independent standing
- Independent squatting
- Half-kneeling
- Kicking a ball
- Handling Explorations and Skills
  - Hands perform different actions
  - Carries objects while walking

Locomotion
- Cross-Lateral Patterns
  - Creeping forward and backward
- Independent walking

Spatial Awareness
- Changes levels
- Changes directions

Communication and Social Interactions
- Postures, gestures, and babbling
- Babbling to first words
- Combining actions, gestures, and words

Baby-Parent
  - Brings and offers a toy or object
  - Ball play

Peer play
  - Object play

Moving Forward

This has been a marvelous year in which you and your baby have been learning together and developing your unique relationship. Your baby created many opportunities for you to gain a deeper understanding and appreciation of the origins and development of human movement, communication, and learning.

Throughout his first year, your baby has embodied his experiences. He has developed a rich, healthy nervous system that enables him to have an array of choices and options in actions, social interactions, and problem solving. In his self-organized play, he has developed a good attention span, initiates and completes his activities, and achieves self-mastery. From this foundation in body movement, your baby is equipped to continue exploring, communicating, and learning.

When you reflect on these incredible accomplishments, I am sure you will agree that this has been a phenomenally exciting year for you as a parent and for your whole family. Now let's look forward to how this unique approach to your baby's development in his first year provides the essential movement foundation for your toddler's continuing development.

Your Amazing Toddler

As your baby celebrates her first birthday, she is moving on to another rung on the ladder of experiential learning. Her balance, body coordination, and physical exuberance are accumulating in new actions, like running across the floor, trying to walk up a steep hill, and learning how to control her momentum going down. She will move on to new adventures tomorrow, like trying to figure out how to navigate her body through, up, and over a jungle gym.

Ball games, with balls of varying sizes, are a favorite activity that challenge her throwing, kicking, and catching skills.

From his body actions in walking, running, and slowing down to stopping, he learns about speed and balance; building a tower of blocks, he learns to balance one block on top of the other. His physical repertoire provides him with an understanding of the cognitive concept of balance that he will need in many future activities.

Action songs are a lot of fun. You will be charmed as you participate and watch your toddler's little fingers touch her eyes, ears, and nose as she tries to coordinate her actions with her words and sing a song at the same time. Her first dance may consist of one foot thumping up and down as she shakes some bells. Jumping, galloping, and hopping are a few months away, but will arrive before you know it. Through these activities, she deepens her understanding of where she is in space, improves the timing of her actions, and organizes these actions into more sophisticated rhythms.

As the two of you engage in more complex social interactions, you, your family, and friends will be encouraging your baby to expand and elaborate on his expressive dialogues. As he learns to coordinate his postures, gestures, and words into a little action song, you will notice that he is doing the same thing in his daily interactions. He is able to imitate simple sounds and words, although you may not completely understand what he is saying. Jabbering on because he enjoys the funniness of the sounds coming out of his mouth, he combines his gestures and babbling into an array of expressive actions that are delightful. You can encourage him by simply giving him your full attention; soon an intelligible word will pop out of his mouth, accompanied by a gesture. The body postures and gestures that accompany his verbalizations will convey his message, and some quizzical little look may become his unique signature expression.

As this book ends, you will recognize your child as a self-confident, curious explorer who will soon literally jump in to meet new challenges. What has made this year so special is that you have enjoyed being with your baby in a unique way. By doing the experiential explorations, you embodied the language your baby knows best—body movement. In your baby's FloorPlay sessions you expanded the meaning of "bonding with your baby" by exploring, interacting, and learning together at your baby's level. Observing your baby closely, you have learned to understand her expressive body language to know what she is communicating. This amazing first year of development has set the stage for your toddler to master new movement skills, elaborate on her social communication skills, and explore new adventures just around the corner.

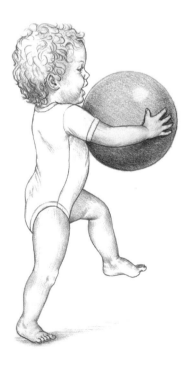

Action plans *baby's ability to create complex strategies, organizing and carrying out a sequence of movements to problem solve in self-motivated play.*

Age-appropriate play *activities that the baby is developmentally ready to accomplish.*

Asymmetrical tonic neck reflex *with rotation of the head to the side, the baby may extend his arm and leg on the face side and flex the opposite arm and leg.*

Bear walk *the baby pushes up onto hands and feet and walks in a cross-lateral pattern.*

Body awareness *kinesthetic and sensory input babies experience from their own movement and tactile body explorations in relation to gravity; essential for body image development.*

Body image *sense of the embodied self developed through interaction and mastery of the environment.*

Body language *commonly used term for expressive nonverbal communication comprised of postures and gestures.*

Breathing coordination *individual way a person breathes to fulfil the unique requirements of her body during varied activities.*

Cervical curve *secondary spinal curve in the neck that develops as the baby lifts her head against gravity; visible in the four-month-old lying on her belly.*

Crawling *unilateral locomotion pattern on the belly, with the arm and leg on the same side of the body flexing and extending together.*

Creeping *cross-lateral locomotion pattern on hands and knees; initiated by a reach of one hand (creeping forward) or by a reach of one foot (creeping backward).*

Cross-lateral movement patterns *movement in which the opposite arm and leg are flexing or extending together, as in creeping, walking, and running.*

Developmental movement *primitive reflexes, righting reactions, equilibrium responses, and basic development movement patterns (spinal, symmetrical, lateral, and cross-lateral). These sequences establish a foundation for our movement activity, perceptual relationships (including spatial orientation and body image), expressive communication, and self-motivated learning.*

Diaphragm *muscle that extends through the body, dividing the chest cavity from the abdominal cavity, that moves upward on exhalation and downward on inhalation during the natural breathing process.*

Equilibrium responses *automatic patterns of response for maintaining balance as a result of an unexpected shifting of one's center of gravity and/or base of support through space, from lying to sitting to standing.*

Exhalation *part of the respiratory cycle in which the diaphragm rises into the rib cage to aid in the expulsion of air from the lungs.*

Extension *straightening or backward movement of the spine or arms/legs.*

Fine motor skills *play with smaller objects that develops eye-hand coordination and manual dexterity.*

Flexion *bending or forward movement of the spine or arms/legs.*

Forearm rotation *ability to turn the forearm so that the hand is palm up and then palm down.*

Gestures *movement of parts of the body to communicate a cue or signal, expressing a feeling, thought, or idea.*

Grasp reflex *baby's strong grip of your finger when you touch the palm of her hand; similarly with toes.*

Grip strength *ability to maintain a firm hold on a toy or object.*

Half-ring, half-long sitting *sitting position in which one leg is flexed and one leg is extended.*

Inhalation *part of the respiratory cycle in which the diaphragm flattens with intake of air into the lungs.*

Integrated movement *merging of posture and gesture that animates the whole body with a consistent movement quality, dynamic, or shape in nonverbal communication.*

Lateral movement patterns *movement of the arm and leg on the same side of the body flexing and extending together, as in belly crawling.*

Lateral pinch *holding a small object between the thumb and the side of curled-up index finger.*

Locomotion *coordinated sequence of movements to go from place to place.*

Long sitting *sitting position in which both legs are fully extended.*

Lumbar curve *secondary spinal curve in the lower back that develops when the baby becomes more vertical with independent sitting and standing.*

Mastery *baby's ability to initiate and successfully complete a problem-solving task in her own time.*

Midline *vertical line dividing the body into right and left symmetrical halves.*

Mimicking *imitating gestures, postures, rhythms, and vocalizing, first within the baby's own repertoire, and then adding novel expressions.*

Moro reflex *baby's startle reaction to a sudden change of position or a loud sound.*

Nonverbal communication *body language expressed through gestures, postures, and integrated movement.*

Oral rooting reflex *baby's nourishment-seeking movement in which he turns in the direction of the stimulation, with his mouth open, in response to gently stroking the area around his mouth.*

Organ system *visceral contents of the body that give a sense of volume to our movement and provide a vital energetic support for our skeletal alignment.*

Palmar grasp *primary reflex underlying the use of the palm to pick up an object.*

Pincer grasp *holding a tiny object between the tips of the thumb and index finger.*

Pivot-prone *extension posture in which the baby balances her whole body on her abdomen—the four-month-old baby's arms are flexed; the five-month-old, while rocking on her abdomen, alternately flexes and extends her arms and looks like she is swimming; the six-month-old extends both arms and legs and looks as if she is flying.*

Pointing *gesture that develops when the baby can isolate his index finger from his thumb; not only a functional skill, but also a communication skill.*

Postures *unified expression of one's whole body, providing a background for gestures.*

Pre-locomotion *movement in a contained space defined by the reach of the baby's arms and legs.*

Preverbal communication *active focusing, postures, gestures, babbling, and vocalizing.*

Primitive reflex *automatic response to a specific stimulus.*

Problem solving *baby's strategy to set up a new situation in order to explore and discover her own solution to a problem and develop mastery through increasing competence.*

Prone *lying on the belly.*

Proprioceptors and kinesthetic receptors *stimuli originating in the bones, joints, ligaments, and muscles that tell us where each part of our body is in relation to the other parts, the position of each part in space, and their quality of relaxation and activity.*

Protective extension *baby's extension of his arms in the same direction to stop a fall when his center of gravity is displaced.*

Protective stepping response *baby's extension of her leg and reaching out with her foot to widen her base of support to stop a fall when her center of gravity is displaced.*

Reach and pull patterns *patterns of elongation that develop through one's relationship to space in reaching out to explore and interact in the environment.*

Righting reactions *establish the vertical axis by lifting and keeping one's head and body upright in relation to gravity and maintaining one's vertical axis in rolling.*

Ring sitting *sitting position in which both legs are flexed.*

Rolling *one of your baby's first locomotion patterns that allows him to change his place in space.*

Self-directed movement *moving or acting with intent; important for developing action plans.*

Self-mastery *baby's ability to regulate her attention, develop a strategy for what she wants to explore, and successfully complete an activity.*

Self-motivated *baby's ability to act on his own curiosity and interest.*

Semi-supine *lying on one's back with both legs flexed and feet flat on the floor.*

Side lying *lying on either side.*

Side sitting *sitting with both legs to one or the other side.*

Spinal alignment *head-to-tail organization.*

Spinal C-curve   *the curve of the infant's spine in utero.*

Spinal extension   *straightening or backward movement of the spine.*

Spinal flexion   *bending or forward movement of the spine.*

Spinal lateral flexion   *side bending of the spine.*

Spinal movement patterns   *antigravity extension, flexion, lateral flexion, and rotation that develop in prone, supine, and side lying and combine in transitions to sitting and standing.*

Spinal rotation   *twisting movement of the spine.*

Spinal S-curve   *in utero the infant's spine is positioned in a primary C-curve. The two reversed curves in the neck and low back develop after birth and are referred to as the secondary curves. The two primary concave curves and the two secondary convex curves give the developed spine an S-shaped curve.*

Supine   *lying on one's back.*

Sustained exhalation   *long out-breath that can be supported by sighing, humming, hissing, or vocalizing vowels.*

Symmetrical movement patterns   *simultaneous flexion or extension of both arms and/or legs together, as in pushing with both hands together in prone to slide backward.*

Tailbone   *small, individual or partly fused, vertebrae that form the lowest part of the spine; also called the coccyx.*

Vertebrae   *bony segments that make up the spinal column.*

Vertical axis   *head-to-tail organization of the spine is designated as the vertical axis in the spatial concept of movement.*

Vestibular system   *sensory organs in the inner-ear system that register the position of the head in relation to gravity and velocity of movement and are critical for all skills requiring balance.*

Visceral system   *the internal functioning of the organs, glands, blood vessels, and nerves that signal their state of rest and activity.*

Visual processing   *focusing, tracking objects, and gathering information; dependent on good head and neck control.*

Voluntary release   *ability to let go of a toy or object with intent.*

Walking   *cross-lateral locomotion pattern with opposite arm and leg moving in relationship to each other (right arm/left leg and left arm/right leg).*

Weight shift   *a change in the body's point of support so that the previous weight-bearing side is now unweighted and free to reposition itself, gesture, or locomote through space.*

Yield and push patterns   *patterns of compression that develop through one's relationship to gravity in which yielding the body's weight occurs before pushing away from the ground.*

227

Aposhyan, Susan. *Natural Intelligence: Body-Mind Integration and Human Development.* Baltimore: Williams & Wilkins, 1999.

Ayres, Jean. *Sensory Integration and the Child.* Los Angeles: Western Psychological Services, 1979.

Bertenthal, Bennett, Joseph Campos, and Rosanne Kermoian. "An epigenetic perspective on the development of self-produced locomotion and its consequences." *Current Directions in Psychological Science* 3:5 (1994).

Bly, Lois. *Motor Skills Acquisition in the First Year: An Illustrated Guide to Normal Development.* Tucson: Communication Skill Builders, 1994.

Brazelton, Berry. *Touchpoints: Your Child's Emotional and Behavioral Development.* Reading, MA: Perseus Books, 1992.

Bushnell, Emily and Paul Boudreau. "Motor development and the mind: The potential role of motor abilities as a determinant of aspects of perceptual development." *Child Development* 64 (1993).

Butterworth, George and Lesley Grover. "The origins of referential communication in human infancy." In L. Weiskrantz, ed., *Thought Without Language.* Oxford: Clarendon Press, 1988.

Campbell, Don. *The Mozart Effect® for Children: Awakening Your Child's Mind, Health, and Creativity with Music.* New York: HarperCollins, 2000.

Campos, Joseph, Rosanne Kermoian, and Marcia Zumbahlen. "Socioemotional transformations in the family system following infant crawling onset." *Emotion and Its Regulation in Early Development: New Directions for Child Development* 55 (1992).

Chugani, Harry. "Metabolic imaging: A window on brain development and plasticity." *Neuroscientist* 5:1 (1999).

Cohen, Bonnie Bainbridge. *Sensing, Feeling, and Action: The Experiential Anatomy of Body-Mind Centering.* Northampton, MA: Contact Editions, 1993.

Damasio, Antonio. *The Feeling of What Happens: Body and Emotion in the Making of Consciousness.* New York: Harcourt Brace, 1999.

Diamond, Marian and Janet Hopson. *Magic Trees of the Mind: How to Nurture Your Child's Intelligence, Creativity, and Healthy Emotions from Birth Through Adolescence.* New York: Penguin Group, 1998.

Feldenkrais, Moshe. *The Elusive Obvious: Or Basic Feldenkrais.* Cupertino, CA: Meta Publications, 1981.

Garvey, Catherine. *Play*. Cambridge, MA: Harvard University Press, 1990.

Gerhardt, Lydia. *Moving and Knowing: The Young Child Orients Himself in Space*. Englewood Cliffs, NJ: Prentice-Hall, 1973.

Goldman, Ellen. *As Others See Us: Body Movement and the Art of Successful Communication*. Lausanne, Switzerland: Gordon and Breach, 1994.

Gorman, David. *The Body Moveable. Volume 1: The Trunk & Head*. Vancouver: Gorman Press, 1981.

Greenspan, Stanley. *Building Healthy Minds: The Six Experiences that Create Intelligence and Emotional Growth in Babies and Young Children*. Cambridge, MA: Perseus Books, 1999.

———. *The Growth of the Mind: And the Endangered Origins of Intelligence*. New York: Addison-Wesley, 1997.

Hannaford, Carla. *Smart Moves: Why Learning Is Not All in Your Head*. Arlington, VA: Great Ocean Publishers, 1995.

Hartley, Linda. *Wisdom of the Body Moving: An Introduction to Body-Mind Centering*. Berkeley: North Atlantic Books, 1995.

Healy, Jane. *Endangered Minds: Why Our Children Don't Think*. New York: Simon & Schuster, 1990.

Johnson, Don, ed. *Bone, Breath & Gesture: Practices of Embodiment*. Berkeley: North Atlantic Books, 1995.

Johnson, Mark. *The Body in the Mind: The Bodily Basis of Meaning, Imagination, and Reason*. Chicago: University of Chicago Press, 1987.

Lee, David. "Body-environment coupling." In Ulric Neisser, ed., *The Perceived Self: Ecological and Interpersonal Sources of Self-Knowledge*. Cambridge: Cambridge University Press, 1993.

Neisser, Ulric. "The self perceived." In Ulric Neisser, ed., *The Perceived Self: Ecological and Interpersonal Sources of Self-Knowledge*. Cambridge: Cambridge University Press, 1993.

Pert, Candace. *Molecules of Emotion: Why You Feel the Way You Feel*. New York: Scribner, 1997.

Stern, Daniel. *The Interpersonal World of the Infant: A View from Psychoanalysis and Developmental Psychology*. New York: Basic Books, 1985.

Stough, Carl and Reece Stough. *Dr. Breath: The Story of Breathing Coordination*. New York: Stough Institute, 1981.

Verny, Thomas R. *The Secret Life of the Unborn Child*. New York: Simon & Schuster, 1981.

———. *Tomorrow's Baby: The Art and Science of Parenting from Conception through Infancy*. New York: Simon & Schuster, 2002.

Guide to Parent-Baby Interactions and Adult Movement Explorations

advances level of exploration, 72
-baby creates tasks, 11, 65, 205
-baby discovers solutions, 65
and body-confidence, 65
and complex games, 217
and current movement skills, 118
and differences between babies, 100
and motivation, 72
and self-directed play, 118
and self-esteem, 11
self-initiated, 72–73
and self-mastery, 72–74
self-motivated, 71, 73 *(See also Play)*
and solutions, 65
and sophisticated plan, 218
and successful completion, 74

R

Reach and pull patterns *(See also Cross-lateral movement; Spinal movement; Symmetrical movement)*
 and elongation, 20, 140–142
 and relationship to space, 141–142
Reflexes, 108
 asymmetrical tonic neck, 50
 grasp, 49
 Moro, 49
 rooting, 29, 31
Repatterning movement, 136
Responses, equilibrium, 108
 and protective extension to the side, 143
 and protective stepping backward, 163
Rhythm, 88, 167–168
 and gestures, 176
 natural, 149
 and response, 88–89
 and slapping hands in creeping, 167
 sophisticated, 222
 and timing, 109
Righting reactions
 lateral head, 86
 pivot-prone, 70–71, 77–78, 84–85, 106–107
Rocking, repetitive, on hands and knees, 125–126, 128
Rolling,
 mastery of, 99
 and shaping rib cage, 87
 to side lying, 60–61, 71, 86
 supine to prone, 108–109
 and vestibular function, 87
Rooting reflex, oral
 and bottle feeding, 30
 and breast feeding, 29
 and head rotation, 30–31

S

Scapulas (shoulder blades), 76
Self
 and body movement, 2
 -confidence, 2, 72, 223
 -directed learner, xiv, 2, 72
 -esteem, 72, 186
 -initiated explorer, 7, 123
 -mastery, 2, 4, 65, 72, 74, 111, 209, 221
 -motivated learner, 1–2
 -motivated play, 100, 106
Sensory awareness, 39
 and information, 72
Side stepping, 163
Sitting
 independent, 101, 116–117, 123, 128–129, 143, 166
 patterns
  half-long, 143, 166
  half-ring, 143, 166
  long, 143, 166
  ring, 116, 143, 166
  side sitting, 166
  W-, 166
Skeletal-muscular system, 47
 and spine, 192
Skills *(See also Handling)*
 fine motor, 57
 functional, 185
Smiling, 39–40, 42–43, 45, 55, 72, 111 *(See also Humor)*
Social interaction
 and active participants, 1 *(See also Communication, baby-to-baby preverbal)*
 and attunement, 88
 body-to-body, 28, 101
 and communication, 12 *(See also Communication, parent-baby nonverbal)*
 complex, 223
 creeping enhances, 151
 and cuddles with grandmother, 56
 and developmental movement, 1
 and emotional development, 31, 74
 and entrainment, xii
 face-to-face, 32, 41–42, 45, 59
 and FloorPlay 6, *(See also FloorPlay)*
 pause before, 10
 and physical actions, 186
 and rhythmic messages, 88–89
 shared, 41 *(See also Communication)*
 takes the lead in, 62, 188
 and touching, 62
 and tuned-in parent, 11, 182
 and unspoken messages, 153, 156
Songs, action, 222
Sounds *(See also Tongue)*
 humming, 50
 making loud, 120

musical, 56
resonant chest vibration, 50, 53
and rhythms, 44, 130
using lips and tongue, 183
whistling and chirping, 56
Space
 and balance and equilibrium, 102
 body, 55
 and body-confidence, 102
 contained, 17
 and movement patterns, 20, 112, 126–127, 129–130
 personal, 99, 139
 reach and pull, in relationship to, 20, 141–142
 and self-confidence, 102
 silent, 85
 and spatial awareness, 149
Spinal curves, 26
 C-curve, 26, 70
 cervical curve, 70, 192
 lumbar curve, 36, 89, 192
 and neck, 70
 S-curve, 192
Spinal movement *(See also Guide to Adult Movement Explorations, 230)*
 and antigravity, 56
 types of
  extension, 85, 106–107
  flexion, 108
  lateral flexion, 83, 92–93
  rotation, 83, 87
 and body image, 19–21
 and core patterns, 110
 and flexibility, 76, 192
 and head-to-tail organization, 102
 and inner organic support, 76–77, 107
 pivot-prone, 77–78, 84–85, 106–107
 and reach and pull patterns, 20, 89–91, 114, 133–134
 and rolling, 108
 and rotation, increased, 196
 and seesaw motion, 26
 and shock-absorbing ability, 192
 and tailbone, 35–36
 and vertebra, 89, 95–96
 and vertical axis, discovery of, 102, 193
 and yield and push patterns, 20, 95–96
Spontaneous play, 7, 72
 and communication, 12
 and parent, 11
Squatting, 198–202
Standing
 bear, 140, 150, 198
 and cruising, 163
 independent, 191, 198, 209
 knee-, 150
 and kneeling, 136
 supported, 140, 150, 157, 163
 and transition, 191
 and walking forward, 191

Stern, Daniel, 88, 188
Stimulation
    of mouth, 72, 176
    over, 118
Stough, Carl, 32
Support
    abdominal, 113
    inner organic, 76, 77
    visceral, 77
Symmetrical movement
    based on spinal patterns, 71
    and body image, 19–21
    and crossing the body's midline, 71
    and locomotion, 113, 115–116, 141
    and midline orientation, 56, 66
    and purposeful movement and play,
        56–57, 66
    and push from both hands, 84, 112,
        124
    and push-ups, 111, 124, 141
    and reach and pull patterns, 181, 205
    and self-initiated play, 72–74
    and vocalizing, 113
    and weight shift, 75
    and yield and push patterns, 20, 71,
        83–84, 110, 140
Systems
    kinesthetic and proprioceptive, 46–47,
        125
    musculoskeletal, 48
    vestibular, 46, 125
    visceral, 46

T

Tactile
    body awareness, 18
    investigation of toys, 47
    stimulation, 71, 82, 106
Talk, at or with, 185
Teasing, 188 (See also Humor)
Time
    through space, 176
    of space, 212, 222
Timing
    improving, 222
    quickness of, 129
    sense of, 99, 167–168
    and simultaneous action, 130
Toddler, Amazing, 221–223
Tongue
    exploration, 33
    and flicking, 45
    and lips, 183
    mimicking, 32, 42
    and movement, 31
    wagging, 32, 43
Toys
    age-appropriate, 65
    mobile, 57
    multicolored links, 65, 73

and play, 118
    rattle, 57
    soft, 57, 62
Transitioning, 198
    sitting to belly crawling, 128
    squatting to bear standing to standing,
        198
Tucking, chin, 56, 69 (See also Head)

U

Unique journey, 13
Upward, moving, 194

V

Verbal (See Language)
Verny, Thomas, xv, 175
Vertical axis
    head-to-tail, 193
    orientation, 212–213
    and rotation around, 214
Vertical orientation to gravity, evolving,
    123
Vestibular organ and walking, 212
Video vignettes, xiv, 3, 22
Visual processing, 17
    active focus, 25
    acute, 29
    and auditory synchronization, 44
    and binocular vision, 71
    and evolving attention, 25
    and eyes as information gatherers, 25
    and eyes beginning to work together,
        41
    and full spectrum color, 66, 73
    and horizontal tracking, 41
    and movement synchronization to
        sound, 44
    and scanning of peripheral field, 126
    and tactile sensations, 17
    and vertical and diagonal tracking, 66
Vitality affects, 88
Vocalizing
    and abdominal protrusion, 59
    with body movement, 62, 112–113
    and unique sounds, 31
    vowels, 45, 59
Voice, tone of, 101

W

Walking
    and attention, 206
    and balance, 206
    bear, 169
    and combining words and gestures, 222
    and cross-lateral connection, 214–215
    and evolving perception of space, 206
    and high guard position, 210

independent, 150, 210
    and kinesthetic feedback, 212
    push off to, 150
    and toe pushing, 210
    and vestibular organ, 212
    and wide base for stability, 210
Weight
    and forearm bearing, 67, 78
    and lateral shift, 88, 125, 131
    and overreaching, 75
    and preparing to reach, 75
    shifting, 75, 78
Workshops
    developmental, 110
    public, 135

Y

Yield and push patterns (See also Lateral
movement; Spinal movement; Symmetrical
movement)
    and compression, 20, 140
    and relationship to gravity, 140

Z

Zumbahlen, Marcia, 151

Amazing Babies®: Moving in the First Year Video

The *Amazing Babies®: Moving in the First Year* video contains the footage that this book is based on. It invites you to participate in following the natural progression of movement and perceptual development during your baby's first year. Like the book, the video is presented chronologically with a summary after each section. You will see the vignettes in full motion with easy-to-follow slow-motion episodes that guide you through longer movement sequences. As expectant, new, or experienced parents, you will gain a fresh perspective on baby development through a body-awareness and movement framework that will stimulate your spontaneity as you communicate with and respond to your unique baby. This is the first video in a series.

What professionals are saying about the video:

"Beverly Stokes has captured in beautifully videotaped vignettes some of the major developmental sequences the baby shows in early life. Her narrative reviews the potential links between these developments in movement and the social, perceptual, cognitive, and emotional reorganizations that take place in the baby's mind and world. I strongly recommend the video for educators and laypersons alike."
Joseph J. Campos, Professor of Psychology, University of California at Berkeley

"This video has some of the most illuminating video footage of babies that you are likely to see. Stokes' explanations are enlightening. It's hard to imagine parents ever watching their baby in the same way after seeing this video."
Today's Parent

Ordering information

To order your *Amazing Babies®: Moving in the First Year* video (ISBN 0-9687900-1-1), contact your local bookstore or go to the Amazing Babies® website at www.amazingbabies.com.